W0009053

THE SHANNON SCHEME

and the Electrification of the Irish Free State

Edited by

Andy Bielenberg

THE LILLIPUT PRESS • DUBLIN

© The Lilliput Press and individual contributors, 2002
Photographs © ESB Archives Photographic Collection and Siemens Archive

First published 2002 by
THE LILLIPUT PRESS LTD
62-63 Sitric Road, Arbour Hill, Dublin 7, Ireland.

A CIP record is available from the British Library.

ISBN 1 845351 007 3 (cased)
ISBN 1 845351 008 1 (paper) 1843510081

Set in 10 on 13 point Adobe Garamond. Design by Karen Carty at Anú Design.
Printed in Dublin by βetaprint

THE SHANNON SCHEME

and the Electrification of the Irish Free State

Contents

Foreword

The Shannon Scheme is perhaps the most important industrial project ever completed in the Irish state and to this day it continues to make a significant contribution to the industrial, commercial and social development of the country. This great achievement continues to evoke a sense of pride and provide a source of inspiration in both ESB and Siemens.

In 2000, Siemens celebrated its seventy-fifth anniversary by signing a unique Archival & Heritage Co-Operation Agreement with ESB. Now, in 2002, as ESB celebrates its own seventy-fifth anniversary, this agreement has borne fruit in the publication of this book. There are several reasons for publishing a book like this. Firstly, it is important as a tribute to the many committed and dedicated people in our respective organizations, heretofore unrecognized, who deserve to receive an acknowledgment of their contribution. Secondly, a book like this adds to the body of knowledge on this subject and can be used as a reference source for those interested in pursuing the topic in greater detail. Thirdly, it celebrates the co-operation between ESB and Siemens that continues to the present day. Finally, it builds on the collaborative effort between ESB, Siemens and University College Cork where the 'Keating and Ardnacrusha' exhibition was staged in May 2000, with some of the main contributors being represented in this book.

We are particularly grateful to Dr Andy Bielenberg, to the contributors and to all those who have helped towards the publication of this book. It has captured the spirit, ingenuity and determination of those responsible for this major landmark in Ireland's social, economic and political development. We are proud of the past achievements of our organizations and we look forward to further co-operation in the years ahead.

Padraig Mc Manus
Chief Executive
ESB

Richard Crowe
Managing Director
Siemens Limited

Acknowledgments

This project started from conversations over lunch in the staff restaurant at the National University of Ireland, Cork, with a fellow member of the Department of History, Hiram Morgan, whose primary motive, I suspect, was to get one of Seán Keating's Ardnacrusha paintings on the cover of *History Ireland*. In this he succeeded, persuading me to pen some of my preliminary thoughts on Keating for the journal. In the process I made contact with the ESB to secure the images, which led to my first meeting with Brendan Delany of ESB and Michael O'Connor of Siemens. Meanwhile, Dermot Keogh asked me to give a paper on the same subject for a conference on Irish art at NUI Cork, which resulted in further research that was augmented for a second paper, given at the History Society in Trinity College Dublin. At this stage I also became involved with Professor Robert Yacamini from the Department of Electrical Engineering and Fiona Kearney of the Visual Arts Office in NUI Cork in organizing an exhibition of Keating's Shannon Scheme paintings and drawings; this was supported by ESB and Siemens – who also contributed archival material – and was held in NUI Cork in May 2000. The exhibition and associated conference received the support from the Keating family, the Crawford Art Gallery in Cork, and the Institution of Electrical Engineers of Ireland.

Along with those mentioned above, the successful publication of this book would not have been possible without the support received from Pat Yeates and Gerry Hampson (ESB), who assisted with the detailed research and completed much of the work in selecting and preparing the illustrations. The following people also helped in various ways: Delo Collier, Dave Dowling, Eddie Mc Nulty, Pauline Holland, Kieran Burns, Brendan Lawlor, Edward Byrne, Benny Counihan, Anne Hogan, the late Ted Dalton, Tina Mc Gee, Frank O'Donoghue, Ken O'Hara, Maureen Cryan, Tracey Dillion, Richard Tobin, Joe Burke, Sean O'Driscoll,

Larry Donald, Rita Bourke, Paddy Stapleton, Pat Treanor, Anne Deignan, David Grundy, Barry Hutch, Ray McIlroy, Tom Martin and Denis Brennan (all ESB); Richard Crowe, Dr Wilfried Feldkerchen, Alexander Kinter, Andy Kinsella Ger O'Byrne, Rodney Tucker, Gerald O'Beirne and Stephen Butterly (all Siemens) for translation work; Justin Keating, the late Michael Keating, Paddy Purcell and John Callanan (both IEI); Dermot Mc Carthy (Bath) for making available his private collection of railway papers; Brendan Pender (Irish Railway Archive), Ella Wilkinson (RHA), Charles Clarke (Crawford College of Art), Donal O Riain, Seamus Maguire, Peter Murray (Crawford Gallery); Sheena Mc Farlane, Bruce Longridge (both Oldham Art Gallery & Museum); Professor Gerard Wrixon, Dr Linda Connolly, Professor Joseph Lee and Professor Tom Dunne (all NUI Cork).

A.B.

McLaughlin, the Genesis of the Shannon Scheme and the ESB

Brendan Delany

Thomas McLaughlin, born in 1896 in Drogheda, is best known as the engineer who conceptualized and initiated the Shannon Scheme; any attempt to understand the genesis of the scheme would be incomplete without some examination of his biography.

He was educated by the Christian Brothers in Synge Street and went on to attend University College Dublin, where he was an intensely competitive student who cared little for non-academic pursuits. After carrying the study of physics to Master's Degree level he became an engineer. His science studies were pursued in University College Dublin, but during his post-graduate years he attended courses in practical engineering subjects in the Royal College of Science. He was appointed to the staff of University College Galway to teach physics, and here he found time to complete a B.E. in electrical engineering in 1922. About the same time he completed his researches on the behaviour of gas bubbles in a fluid subjected to the action of an electric field, and he was awarded a Ph.D. in 1923. It has been claimed that while lecturing in UCG he was strongly influenced by Frank Sharman Rishworth, Professor of Civil Engineering there, who was subsequently appointed by the government of the Irish Free State in 1925 to act as Chief Engineer on the Shannon Scheme, and that Rishworth actively encouraged McLaughlin to investigate the possibility of implementing a major hydro-electric scheme on the Shannon.[1]

Before his Ph.D. had been conferred, McLaughlin had embarked on his engineering career. He recalled:

> No sincere student could have lived through that whole period of intense national enthusiasm without feeling a passionate desire to do all in his power to assist in national reconstruction, and in the building up of the country by development from within. It was with this intense feeling I began my career abroad, and the ideal never for a moment left me until it brought me home again to see the Shannon Scheme realised. It was little credit to me – I could know no mental peace, no sense of self-fulfilment until my mission in life, as it had then become to me, was realised. Everything I saw abroad, everything I read of, brought just one thought to my mind – can this development be applied at home? Could we have this in Ireland? Such were the natural yearnings of a youth of that inspiring period.[2]

In 1922 he went to London hoping to acquire practical experience in the British electrical industry, but without success. He was offered a job prospecting for oil in Texas, and another in a munitions factory, but he turned them down. Shortly afterwards he joined the German firm Siemens-Schuckert, and later that year he was sent to Berlin to study the design of power plants, the manufacture of electrical machinery and all the problems relating to transmission and distribution. During his time in Berlin he also availed of opportunities to visit power plants in operation and under construction:

> In Bavaria I saw a network similar to our Shannon network, fed by water plants similar to the Shannon. What impressed me most, probably, was the network supplying the province of Pomerania, a province with an area of about half that of our territory at home. Pomerania resembled our country in being almost entirely agricultural. An electricity network extended like a spider's web all over the country, supplying 60 towns, 1,500 villages and rural areas, and close on 3,000 farms. To this area I went and studied for myself on the spot, always with the query in my mind – why not so in Ireland? From reading and from discussions I learned of the large-scale electricity networks of other countries, of Sweden and Switzerland, of Italy and France, of Canada and of the United States. ... Quickly came

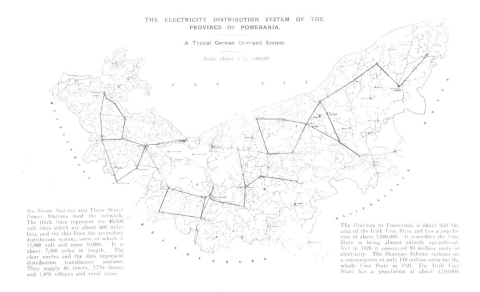

THE ELECTRICITY DISTRIBUTION SYSTEM OF THE
PROVINCE OF POMERANIA.

A Typical German Overland System.

Scale about 1 to 800,000.

Six Steam Stations and Three Water Power Stations feed the network. The thick lines represent the 40,000 volt lines which are about 600 miles long and the thin lines the secondary distribution system, some of which is 15,000 volt and some 10,000. It is about 7,000 miles in length. The clear circles and the dots represent distribution transformer stations. They supply 60 towns, 2,750 farms, and 1,490 villages and rural areas.

The Province of Pomerania is about half the area of the Irish Free State and has a population of about 1,800,000. It resembles the Free State in being almost entirely agricultural. Yet in 1920 it consumed 93 million units of electricity. The Shannon Scheme reckons on a consumption of only 110 million units for the whole Free State in 1931. The Irish Free State has a population of about 3,100,000.

■ Map of Pomerania.
Source: The Shannon Scheme, Considered in its National Economic Aspect (1924).

the determination that at home in Ireland we must have a national electricity network reaching to our cities, towns and villages, and on out to the rural areas. My country, of which I was so intensely proud, must not lag behind other lands. The people in our remote villages must have the comforts which villagers in other lands enjoyed. Electricity, the great key to the economic uplift of the country, must be provided on a national scale, cheap and abundant. I saw Germany struggling to reconstruct its national economy after being beaten in world war. Having lost large coalfields, she had turned to exploit waterpower and brown coal. I heard how every land generated power from its own resources; how Italy, through lack of coal, in the Great War had been thrown completely back on water power; how Sweden and Switzerland relied on their native water power; how Finland used her water power and her wood fuel; how Norway, a country as poor as our own, could buy coal as cheaply from England as we could, but preferred to develop her own water power. And the more I heard of the national power policy of other countries the more I realised the necessity of developing our own national resources, be they coal or peat or water power. A national electricity network could easily be constructed, but a national source of power supply must be found and exploited to feed that network.[3]

He soon ruled out the option of using peat or coal as the basis for an immediate solution to Ireland's future energy needs, coming quickly to the conclusion that hydro-electric power was a more realistic option for utilizing native resources in the Irish Free State. Working in a number of the central departments of Siemens in Berlin, he was allowed to pursue his own programme of work and study, and used this opportunity to broaden his knowledge of electrical generation, transmission and distribution systems. The company's hydropower department was particularly strong, with Otto Uitting exerting a major influence. Uitting subsequently made a major contribution to the Shannon Scheme as one of the key Siemens engineers working on site.

McLaughlin was able to draw upon the work and findings of some notable predecessors who had explored the possibility of using the Shannon as a source of electricity. As early as 1844, Robert Kane concluded that 34,000 horsepower could be harnessed from the lower Shannon.[4] In 1875 an article in *The Engineer* made the case for utilizing the fall in the river between Killaloe and Limerick to generate electricity. In 1901 the Frazer Scheme[5] was published, to be followed by Dicks' proposals in 1902.[6] A further proposal was based on the construction of four power stations between Killaloe and Limerick.[7] Crowley & Partners outlined a scheme that was based on utilizing both the Liffey and the Shannon.[8] Cost and political considerations as much as criticism of the design features played a significant part in ensuring that none of these schemes got off the ground.

McLaughlin used Chaloner Smith's data flows from the river Shannon, which he analyzed along with the proposals in the earlier studies.[9] He also had the benefit of some knowledge of other continental hydro-powered schemes, which he acquired while working with Siemens. This enabled him to develop acceptable technical solutions to flow-control and storage problems, which withstood technical scrutiny, in addition to sustaining the economic arguments for his final proposals. His engineering colleagues in Siemens became highly interested in his work as it unfolded. A rough study was carried out which he later referred to as a 'practical exercise'; the results of this work confirmed that some of his conceptual solutions should work in practice. This prospect was also

■ Dr T.A. McLaughlin.
*Source: ESB Archives
Photographic Collection.*

confirmed by the work of his colleagues in the hydroelectric department of Siemens who had considerable experience of evaluating all kinds of schemes in many different countries.

He returned to Ireland in December 1923. Because of his personal friendship with many government ministers, including McNeill, FitzGerald, McGrath, O'Higgins and Hogan, he was allowed to present his proposals to the most influential members of government, with the result that Siemens was given the green light to prepare a paper detailing its full proposals. These proposals were later adapted to become a White Paper and were evaluated by an independent international team of four experts appointed by the government. The expert team charged with undertaking a technical and commercial evaluation approved the plans subject to some minor modifications.

As Duffy has written, McLaughlin's major feat was 'developing a practical, well-thought-out plan that was achievable and would work, and then convincing people to act on it'.[10] In 1924 there was still active interest in implementing a Liffey hydroelectric power supply for the Dublin region, and four private bills to this end were put before a committee of the Dáil. McLaughlin convinced the government that a national solution for the production of electricity would be preferable to a local one that served Dublin and its environs only.[11]

> The Liffey river, the development of which was under discussion at home, did not interest me further, it seemed too small to be of any service for national supply – and I selected for investigation the largest source of water power in the country – the Shannon. In the various waterpower reports we had Chaloner Smith's flow figures on the river, and I wrote home and purchased large-scale survey and geological maps of the area. On the principle of securing the maximum utilisation of the river it was decided to project, using the total fall from Lough Derg to Limerick. Preliminary calculations and rough costings showed that with this design we could get a much larger output from the river than anything previously contemplated to my knowledge, and the rough cost figures appeared reasonably economic. The Shannon Scheme was in embryo.[12]

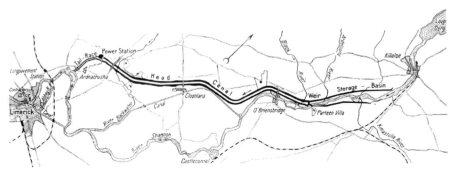

■ General Plan of Scheme.
Source: Siemens, Progress on the Shannon, Number 1, October 1926.

There was determined opposition from the Institution of Civil Engineers of Ireland to McLaughlin's proposal, but the government satisfied public criticism by having it examined and approved by four experts drawn from Switzerland and Sweden.[13] Having succeeded in getting his proposals accepted and implemented,

■ Supervising the installation of a turbine.
Source: ESB Archives Photographic Collection.

McLaughlin then moved thinking forward by presenting proposals for the longer-term management of the electricity system within the state. McGilligan considered various options – setting up a new government department to manage the activity; allowing a private enterprise in Ireland to take over responsibility; putting a large foreign undertaking in charge. This third possibility was given serious consideration as he visited the United States and met several interested parties, some of whom offered him bribes in an effort to win favour for their respective companies. McLaughlin, however, urged the government to consent to his view that such rapid development could only be achieved through unified control of production and distribution, and this provided the impetus for the legislation in 1927 that created the Electricity Supply Board, the first semi-state body in Ireland. He was appointed as the first Managing Director.

■ Construction work in progress.
Source: ESB Archives Photographic Collection.

The challenge facing him in this new post was immense. His main task was to oversee the setting up of an organization, which took over the newly built power station at Ardnacrusha, and in a number of other smaller generating stations, many of which were privately owned. In addition, a complex distribution system which had been based on a DC system had to be replaced with an AC system. Networks had to be constructed in towns where none existed. Private undertakings had to be purchased where the owners agreed to sell. Wiring systems had to be re-configured for houses and industry and promotional tariff rates devised. McLaughlin appointed E.A. Lawler as his public-relations manager: the first appointment of its kind in Europe. McLaughlin, Lawler and his senior management team quickly set about expanding consumer demand for the power that was to come on stream from Ardnacrusha in 1929.

McLaughlin's approach to marketing was distinctly refreshing, and he was ably assisted by his wife, who became the first President of the Irish Women's Electrical Association, which promoted the use of electricity for household use. O'Beirne, the historian of Siemens (Ireland), argues that this kind of initiative proved to be a successful part of the marketing strategy, helping to raise electricity sales from 43 million kWh in 1930 to 218 million kWh in 1937.[14] McLaughlin was able to appoint a few engineers on a contractual basis for a limited period, who had experience working abroad, notably in Sweden, Germany and Canada. These engineers played a critical role in transferring their technical knowledge to the engineering staff who were recruited mainly from the newly emerging cadre of Irish-trained engineers. ESB rapidly expanded and before the end of 1931 the organization had created thirteen new District Offices, each with a District Engineer and District Accountant. These had been created around the country to ensure local staff with local knowledge were at hand to tackle any emerging problems.

McLaughlin earned a reputation for getting things done, but given the rapid expansion of ESB the organization found it difficult to control costs. Even McGilligan, the Minister for Industry and Commerce, who had been a prominent supporter and close friend of McLaughlin, now felt obliged to insist that proper controls and accounting procedures be put in place. This had to be done before the organization could be allowed to proceed further with such rapid expansion plans. This stipulation led to a clash between the government and the ESB in relation to financial autonomy, with the net result that Murphy stepped down from his role as Chairman.

His successor, Browne, quickly became engaged in a confrontation with McLaughlin. Browne at this point concluded that 'Dr McLaughlin as Managing Director had assumed full authority to run the Board subject to the General Board meeting. My predecessor had been ousted from his true position and had become a purely nominal Chairman.'[15] This situation could not continue indefinitely, and in May 1931 McLaughlin, under pressure from the government, resigned from his position as of Managing Director.

McLaughlin recalled this episode and its aftermath as follows:

> On May 13th 1931 I resigned from the Board rather than be removed from office. My friend the Minister stated his views at the time in the Dáil and they are recorded in the official debates. Mr James M. Fay had been on

■ Presentation to Dr T.A. McLaughlin by the staff of the ESB of a silver model of Ardnacrusha Power Station. In front are, from the left, Mr P.J. Dempsey, secretary of the ESB, Dr McLaughlin, Mr J. O'Farrell and Mr B. O'Sullivan. Also included are Messrs L.A. Lawler, M. Matthews, P.J. Corr, G. O'Callaghan, J.C. Davidson, P. Flanagan, F. Algar and P. McDonald.
Source: Irish Independent 7 May 1932.

the Board with me as Director of Civil Works. He remained on the Board and took the title Technical Director. The opposition in the Dáil at that time (Fianna Fáil) returned to power the following year as the government, and I was re-appointed to the Board in August 1932. I was not re-appointed Managing Director but given the title Technical Director and remained as such, in harness with my colleague Mr Fay, for twenty-five years. Looking back on this hiatus in my career, I feel the history of the Board at that time might have been very different, had I only had the good sense to accept a proposal put forward in writing to me personally in February 1930, by the Minister – that I accept Mr Fay as Joint Managing Director and accept equal status with Mr Fay as a Director. I was not prepared to accept either of these proposals and relations became strained.[16]

His resignation as Managing Director provoked a very unusual gesture from his management colleagues and staff in the ESB, who collected such a sizeable amount in contributions that they were able to commission a silver replica scale model of the power plant at Ardnacrusha, which was presented to him at a special function in the Gresham Hotel on 6 May 1932. This was indeed a remarkable show of solidarity and support, not just because the model presented is one of the finest pieces of silver craftsmanship ever produced in this country, but also because it was a public event, and as such it did not go unnoticed by

■ Concrete work for intake building.
Source: ESB Archives Photographic Collection.

■ Erecting the first pole of the Rural Electrification Scheme at Kilsallaghan, Co. Dublin, on 5 November 1944.
Source: ESB Archive Photographic Collection.

the press.[17] It is probable that the widespread coverage of the retirement was a factor that the new Fianna Fáil government took into account when Sean Lemass re-appointed McLaughlin to the Board of the ESB in August 1932.[18] This was to fill the vacancy caused by the death of Foley. Browne protested to de Valera about McLaughlin's re-appointment, but it went ahead and it led to several boardroom clashes about the allocation of responsibilities between Browne (as chairman) and McLaughlin. The work of electrifying the country proceeded.

In early 1930 McLaughlin had had a series of unofficial meetings with William Scott, Permanent Secretary at the Ministry of Commerce in Northern Ireland, and also with Whysall, the Belfast City Engineer, to review proposals in relation to the Erne Scheme and the feasibility of setting up an inter-connector.[19] In October 1930 McLaughlin and Whysall both addressed the Institute of Electrical Engineers, highlighting the case for greater co-operation. McLaughlin declared: 'My one ambition in connection with the Shannon Scheme is to see inter-connection to Northern Ireland.' He explained that this could lead to cheaper electricity for consumers on both sides of the border. That such practical co-operation was eventually achieved with the construction of the hydroelectric scheme on the Erne was due in no small measure to his talents as a persuasive leader. Thereafter, co-operation between the ESB and Northern Ireland Elec-tricity continued. The use of an inter-connector following the successful completion of the Erne Scheme was based on the concept of risk-sharing between two distinct and independent systems, which reduced excess capacity and the investment required for additional generating capacity. It also improved the security of supply in the two jurisdictions until it was targeted by terrorists on both sides of the border. Many years later economic considerations again became paramount, and the inter-connector was restored in 1995.

The original intention of the Shannon Scheme was for the electrification of the entire state: not just town-dwellers, but the rural population as well. The initial phase focused on bringing supply to urban centres, but throughout the 1930s McLaughlin still aspired to supply rural areas. In a lecture to the Institute of Engineers in 1940 McLaughlin once again set out his determination to see his original plans being carried through to the large sections of the rural population who were still without electricity.[20]

McLaughlin, with the assistance of a small project team under the initial guidance of Dowling, presented a preliminary report to the ESB Board of Directors in 1942, and this document served as the basis for a report on rural electrification, which was subsequently published and presented to government in 1944 as a white paper.[21] It was accepted, with the necessary legislation being approved in 1945, but its implementation had to be delayed until 1946 because of wartime shortages. In the interim McLaughlin and his Board appointed William Roe to manage the scheme, with Dowling as his deputy.[22] A distinct project group was established within the ESB and the initial financial provision

■ Dr. T.A. McLaughlin.
*Source: ESB Archives
Photographic Collection.*

was for an expenditure of ir£5m (of which one half was provided by way of state subsidy).

McLaughlin drew heavily from his experience in Siemens when it came to planning the rural electrification programme. He had made a particular study of similar schemes in Germany, Denmark, Sweden and the USA, but he was particularly interested in the manner in which funding was organized in Ontario, Canada. The Ontario Scheme utilized two forms of subsidy: initial capital funding, and a subvention that was variable but ensured there was an upper limit on what each customer had to contribute by way of a fixed charge. In Ireland Dowling planned the programme on an area-by-area basis.[23] The country was divided into 792 areas, with priority being given to those that would potentially yield the highest revenue in relation to the capital cost of the network. Supply was offered to all houses in a selected area by specially appointed rural canvassers. Those who agreed to take supply were not expected to make a capital contribution towards the costs, but they had to agree to pay special service charges which were additional to the standard two-monthly fixed charge. But charges were implemented in a graded manner to even out the tariff structure which occurred because of the differences in the capital costs associated with bringing supply to individual customers. The rural scheme was ultimately to reach practically every home in the Irish countryside, and it was probably one of the most important developments in twentieth-century Irish social history.[24]

Hydro schemes were completed on the Liffey, the Erne and the Lee. A small oil-burning station was built in North Wall in Dublin. A Turf Development Board was created in order to exploit another native resource, bringing peat from native bogs into productive use. Before this could happen, Bord na Mona and ESB had to devise and adapt an almost new technology for peat generation. The debate about the utilization of peat and the technology requirements for the development of the new peat stations went on for a long time and placed a heavy burden on McLaughlin and his fellow directors, particularly Fay and Laurence Kettle. Major stations were built in Portarlington and Allenwood, and later stations, which utilized an even newer technology to burn milled peat, were constructed in Ferbane, Rhode, Shannonbridge and Lanesboro. All these stations were supplied with native fuel and staffed by local labour and they became a focus of pride in their respective communities, which had little other industry to help offset the social scourge of emigration. Four small 5MW stations which burned hand-won turf were built largely as a social contribution to the depressed rural areas on the western seaboard in Gweedore, Screeb, Milltown Malbay and Cahirciveen; these outlasted the others in terms of longevity. A generating station was built in Arigna to burn coal that was mostly graded as inferior quality, known as crow coal. New steam stations were also built at Marina in Cork and at Ringsend in Dublin.

By the close of the fifties, when McLaughlin retired, the ESB was meeting a demand for electricity that had multiplied forty-fold since 1930. As the system expanded the Board issued its first public stocks, which were enthusiastically supported by small investors, indicating widespread confidence in the ESB.

During his career at the ESB McLaughlin was always greatly concerned for the welfare of all staff, but he had a particular loyalty to engineers, and was very proud to be able to play a leading role in the Institution of Engineers. He had a reputation for having little patience with administrators, undoubtedly due to the fact that he was a doer as much as a thinker. He was elected President of Cumann na Innealtoiri in 1946 and of the Institute of Civil Engineers of Ireland in 1950.[25] In his Presidential address to the Institution of Civil Engineers on 6 November 1950 he articulated some life-long beliefs when he stated:

> It is clear from the argument that administrative control of the professions will tend, in time, to destroy the very concept and spirit of them. In this country we are only at the preliminary stage where control has been in the main achieved; the results will flow from it and will take some decades to show themselves fully and leave their mark on the social and economic life of the country. Meanwhile, the public is little interested. But it is the duty of those of us who realise the grave damage to progress which will result from this policy, to indict it. Happiness in life consists in the exercise of initiative, in a sense of freedom and creation in one's work. This was enjoyed by the professional engineer of my youth. Today, I think I am voicing the sentiments of the elders of the profession when I say it has largely disappeared. It is replaced by a sense of frustration; by a sense of growing helplessness in this age of controls, created out of the opportunities by the periods of emergencies and world conflict and out of the vanities of men.[26]

It was said of him that he demanded loyalty and enthusiasm from his staff.[27] It is abundantly clear that he received both, and this was due to people's confidence in him as a leader, and to his nature, which was both firm and kind. Despite all McLaughlin had been through with his resignation and re-appointment, he chose to remain loyal to the ESB. There can be little doubt that a man of his stature could have commanded a salary greatly in excess of what the government felt able to authorize; his willingness to serve as ESB Technical Director represented both an acceptance of reduced freedom within the organization and a very considerable financial sacrifice. In later years, when he no longer acted as a full-time director to the ESB, McLaughlin engaged in a wide range of business activities, from civil engineering contracting to pharmaceuticals and oil distribution. He was appointed as a Director of Irish Shell Ltd and was also Chairman of the Board of Aspro-Nicholas of Ireland.

On 16 February 1957, the day after his death, the well-known broadcaster P.P. O'Reilly paid the following tribute to McLaughlin on Radio Telefís Eireann:

The man who died in Spain yesterday has left Ireland the greatest physical memorial that any Irishman has given his country. For it was he who harnessed the Shannon and made it produce light and power. In 1923, working as a trainee engineer at the Siemens-Schuckert factory in Germany, the 26-year-old Tommy McLaughlin saw what Germany was doing harnessing electric power from the flow and fall of water and bringing this power on vast networks to every corner of the land. He asked himself why? Why not so in Ireland, where only one in forty homes had electric light? He prepared his plans and returned at Christmas 1923 to a country dismayed and shattered by the civil war: he cajoled the parties together – the reluctant government – the hopeful German firm. When they needed money to do the preliminary surveys – the Germans had none nor indeed the government – he got it himself through a personal overdraft from a bank manager in Limerick. Then, backed by the government and particularly by the new Minister, Patrick McGilligan, the work began. Five thousand men created the great barriers of Ardnacrusha and Parteen, and our largest river was stopped in its course. 'It was Tommy McLaughlin who thought it all up,' said Doctor McGilligan.[28]

The Irish Free State and the Electricity Industry, 1922-1927

Lothar Schoen

When the Irish Free State was established late in 1922, the electricity industry was still very underdeveloped. In the wake of the Civil War there were many competing claims on the state's meagre financial resources. Although there was a general consensus among politicians that available resources should be assessed with the view to creating greater self-reliance in energy, there was far less unanimity on how this should be achieved. Cumann na nGaedheal, who formed the first government, initially took a laissez-faire approach in economic matters, favouring private enterprise over state intervention. This chapter examines the circumstances in which the government over a five-year period dramatically altered its stance, moving uncharacteristically towards a more interventionist approach in the realm of electrification.

While in the towns and cities there were a host of electricity supply undertakings, in villages and in rural areas there were only a few small generating stations delivering electricity at a high price. A number of industrial producers located in regions without electricity still depended on water, steam or internal combustion engines for motive power.[1] In agriculture, the mainstay of the economy, scarcely any farms had electric light or power, limiting productivity and incomes in that sector.

It must have been apparent that only widespread electrification could bring about essential improvements in productivity, profitability, and working conditions.

■ Mr Patrick McGilligan, Minister for Industry and Commerce 1924-1932.
Source: ESB Archives Photographic Collection.

There were few countries in Europe at that time where the population was as poorly served as in the Irish Free State in terms of the availability of electrical energy.[2] Annual Irish consumption per head in 1926 was 23 kWh (16 kWh in the Free State and 43 kWh in Northern Ireland). If Dublin and Belfast are left out, the per capita consumption for the rest of Ireland was only 6 kWh. A good comparison may be made with Hungary, where the supply of electricity at that time was not much better. With a population of 8.5 million (of which 4.8 million had no electricity), the annual per capita consumption in 1925 was 26 kWh, or, leaving out the major cities, only 10 kWh.[3] The Irish Free State had the lowest consumption of electricity in Europe, with the exception of Portugal.[4]

In 1923 there were about 300 electricity producers in the Irish Free State, generating current from coal, oil, gas or hydro-energy, often only for their own use, or for sale to a small circle of customers in the neighbourhood. There were only 91 power stations for public electricity supply in 1924.[5] Larger stations were predominantly located in Dublin and its suburbs, as well as in Cork and Limerick.[6] Of the 91 public power stations, just four generated alternating current. The others used direct current, which could only be transmitted economically over a few hundred yards. Prices were generally very high.[7] In many districts hydropower plants were very inefficient and costly. There was a relatively small annual electricity requirement in many districts with a limited customer base. The Bandon Hydro-Electric Undertaking in Co. Cork provides a good example of the difficulties facing such stations. Because of wide variations in water flow and a lack of storage potential, a gas machine of 60 kW and battery had to be installed, raising the cost of the enterprise.[8]

Despite the shortcomings of existing hydropower sources, there was a consensus that hydro-electrical power should be used to reduce energy dependence on British coal, thereby improving the balance of payments.[9] As a matter of priority,

■ Dublin City Power Station at Fleet Street, about 1900.
Source: ESB Archives Photographic Collection.

the continuity of electricity supply also needed to be secured, and for this reason dependence on external primary energy sources needed to be scaled down. It was also clear that with growing demand for electricity over the coming decades, this dependence could rapidly increase if the country was tied to coal-powered plants. By May 1923 already, the conclusions and recommendations of the major commissions for the investigation of the country's hydropower were under consideration in the Dáil. The Seanad requested the government to create better conditions for the erection of efficient hydropower projects, and carry out more detailed research to investigate its potential.[10]

The rivers that emerged as the main contenders for development were the Shannon and the Liffey. Several projects had been proposed by private enterprises and by Dublin Corporation in the first half of the 1920s, centred largely on Dublin. The possibilities of developing the Shannon or a national grid were not seriously considered by private undertakings or the state prior to the proposal from McLaughlin and Siemens.[11] An important advantage for the Liffey lay in its proximity to Dublin, the principal load centre within the state. Plans for such a Dublin-centred scheme had been considered for some time. But the government had many other pressing issues absorbing its attention. Initially, it left the field of electrification mainly to that group lobbying for the development of the Liffey. There were others, apart from those motivated purely by profit in the lucrative Dublin market, who were convinced of the advantages of a scheme centred on the Liffey. With a view to achieving the necessary legislative empowerment, a number of these groups approached the Dáil in 1923 with their plans to harness the Liffey. A number of private bills were being considered in the Dáil, aimed essentially at the development of Liffey hydropower by companies established for this purpose.[12] These schemes only considered Dublin and its immediate hinterland, giving little consideration to the rest of the country.

■ Transporting the runner of one of the Francis turbines from Longpavement, 1928.
Source: ESB Archives Photographic Collection.

None of the politicians before 1924 had considered the possibilities of a comprehensive national electrification programme. As late as 1925, Sir John Purser Griffith's Dublin Electricity Supply bill was under consideration,[13] after the Dublin Corporation proposal had been withdrawn. The 'Griffith bill' was not, however, destined to make further progress, as the government had begun to consider the merits of the Shannon proposal.[14] At the end of 1923 and beginning of 1924, the government was presented for the first time with a proposal for a project which envisaged the utilization of Shannon hydropower alone, north of Limerick, and the countrywide distribution of electrical energy from a large power station located there, exploiting the far greater energy reserves of the Shannon. The initiator of this project, Dr McLaughlin, with the assistance of specialists from Germany, succeeded in convincing the government of the technical and commercial feasibility of his plans. The decision to proceed with the Shannon Scheme proposal was heavily influenced by the aspiration to supply all parts of the population. The fact that the scheme assumed a 'national' character was critical.

■ W.T. Cosgrave, President of the Irish Free State.
Source: History of the ESB (1984).

McLaughlin was familiar with a number of Dáil deputies, and so had no difficulty in meeting members of the government.[15] On 28 December 1923 he met Cosgrave, who was initially unreceptive to his proposals. Ultimately McLaughlin, and other supporters of the Shannon Scheme, succeeded in having it given more detailed consideration, and a further meeting with Cosgrave was arranged. Participants at this meeting (on 26 January 1924) included McGrath (the Minister for Industry and Commerce until March 1924), Blythe (the Minister for Finance) and Kennedy (the Attorney General). McLaughlin pointed out explicitly at this meeting that he could not expect further expenditure of time and money by Siemens-Schuckert on the project, if it were not possible for him to convince the firm of the serious intent of the government. Their reticence was only overcome when it was agreed that the scheme would be technically and commercially assessed by a team of neutral internationally recognized experts.[16]

Early in 1924 contact was established between the Siemens directors and the Free State government (notably the Department of Industry and Commerce). The government requested a detailed report from Siemens-Schuckertwerke for an electricity scheme to supply the entire country; this was submitted on 1

■ Erection of the superstructure of the upper lock as viewed from the right headrace bank. *Source: ESB Archives Photographic Collection.*

October 1924.[17] Meanwhile, in March 1924, McGrath had been replaced in his position as Minister for Industry and Commerce by Patrick McGilligan, a member of the Dáil since November 1923, who over the following decades held several ministerial positions (including Industry and Commerce, External Affairs and Finance). He had been one of the most prominent and articulate supporters of the scheme since 1923, when McLaughlin had sought him out in London, where he was the Secretary of the Irish High Commission. Although McGilligan was a layman in the field of technology (his studies had been in law), he familiarized himself with the technical issues for the debates on the Shannon Scheme in the Dáil, and this undoubtedly played a major part in rapidly promoting the merits of the scheme.

In October 1924 the Siemens proposal was submitted to the international experts. The first World Power Conference in London in 1924 had provided an opportunity to select and engage them: McGilligan travelled there to make the relevant contacts. German experts were not hired, for obvious reasons, while North Americans were not considered because it was decided that all protagonists in the First World War should be excluded. The appointment of Irish experts was ruled out, subjecting the government to severe criticism from Irish engineers, who argued they had a long and respectable tradition of engineering and the necessary experience and expertise.[18] The government, however, insisted that the requisite scientific and technical expertise and experience from abroad would be absolutely necessary to ensure the success of the project.

Before the government could finally award the contract to Siemens, consent had to be sought from the Dáil, which also had to make the necessary financial provisions (amounting to £5.2 million for the 'first partial development' of the scheme). This gave rise to extensive debates on the scheme and the wider issue of electrification. However, Brennan, the Secretary of the Department of Finance, had grave reservations about the lack of consultation by the government with his Department on how exactly the scheme was to be financed, since it and the establishment of the ESB were the most costly interventions by the state in this era. He found this situation intolerable, which contributed in no small way to his declining relationship with the Minister for Finance, Blythe, and ultimately to his resignation as Secretary in 1927. The financing of the Shannon Scheme was one of the few instances in the 1920s when the stringent views of Finance, the premier Department in the civil service, were simply over-ruled. The experts summarized their findings and suggested alterations in a document published in March 1925. Siemens accepted these requests, and subsequently implemented most of them, which led to some increase in the cost projections.[19]

The Dáil debates revealed that there were essentially four different attitudes to the scheme.[20] There were those who fully supported it, and those who were for it in principle, but called for various improvements. There were opponents of the scheme who had doubts about its feasibility, either on technical or commercial grounds, and those who, simply from self-interest, had a preference for the Liffey project.

Those who opposed German involvement were supported by some anti-German elements in the British press. The *Daily Mail*, for example, in July 1924 alleged, under the heading 'German Intrigue in Ireland – Bid for Economic Control', that the German 'Siemens Syndicate' wished to set up an electricity monopoly in Ireland and control Irish industry from Germany. Profits from Ireland would be used, it was claimed, to strengthen German industry. Furthermore, it was pointed out that the same German syndicate had been engaged in extending its tentacles into Switzerland, and had taken control of most of the hydro-electric resources of the northern cantons. It could now turn its attention to the Irish Free State. The article also alleged that the Germans were looking for control of Northern Ireland, and reassured readers that the government there would not yield![21] Other English publications, however, took a more balanced appraisal of German involvement, conceding that German expertise and Irish initiative, rather than anti-English sentiment, were the critical factors behind the planning stages of the Scheme.[22]

■ Dr G. Probst, chief engineer of Siemens-Schuckertwerke on the Shannon.
Source: ESB Archives Photographic Collection.

Regarding the major technical difficulties that would have to be faced, attempts were frequently made to create the impression that the participating firms would be unable to resolve these. It was alleged that the proposed dams were too weak at certain points, and that dam bursts or sabotage would be inevitable. There were also a considerable number of objective assessments of it by critics who had genuine concerns about its feasibility. The Farmers Party, for example, who were not set against the project in principle (given the benefits to agriculture), had a tendency to be cautious about aspects of the plan.[23]

Despite the many reservations expressed, with the unanimity of Cumann na nGaedheal on the Shannon legislation, the passing of the bill was ensured. Nevertheless, it was important for the government that legislation on a matter of such national significance should be introduced with minimal opposition. Consequently it went to great lengths to convince the opposition members to support it. In December 1924 McGilligan had made a detailed presentation of the scheme to the Dáil.[24] His presentation was based on the report of Siemens and that of the experts.[25] He stressed that, in contrast to the Liffey projects, the Shannon one was a 'national scheme'. The great majority of members shared this sentiment, more especially since the Expert Commission judged this approach to be the wiser course of action.[26] McGilligan on 19 December 1924 also spoke out against the fear of a 'German economic stranglehold', which he declared to be unfounded.[27] He pointed out that political freedom without economic freedom signified little. He expressed the view that the Shannon Scheme was the most important undertaking within the state since its foundation.

There was criticism of the procedure adopted by the government in awarding a large state contract without putting it out to tender.[28] When the concept of the scheme and the electrification of the entire state was presented to the government early in 1924, it was open to the government to arrange to have a specification prepared by suitable consulting engineers incorporating its requirements. The government was obviously impressed by the Siemens project, and decided early on to pursue it immediately. Thus, at the start, all other conceivable competitors were ruled out. In the Dáil, to a related question, Cosgrave gave the answer: 'No firm other than Messrs Siemens has sought an opportunity to put forward proposals relating to the Shannon, and consequently no other firm has been given that opportunity.'[29]

The White Paper, and comments by the government, clearly indicate that the Cabinet took the view that the concept and initiative for the Shannon Scheme were the intellectual property and resource of McLaughlin and Siemens. McGilligan's memorandum of 16 June 1925 to the Minister for External Affairs, FitzGerald, following an expression of interest in the contract by Americans, was a clear expression of the government's attitude: 'The German firm is now about to reap the reward of its enterprise, its scientific methods of investigation, its engineering repute and its tenacity in face of an unenthusiastic reception by the Irish Government.' He went on: 'But it is clear that our natural leaning towards America cannot bring us to the point of letting that country in to exploit other people's discoveries. We must reward diligence and enterprise no matter from what source they come.'[30] In the Seanad, tribute was paid to the German engineers whose 'ability and brilliance has made Germany one of the greatest economic forces in the modern world'.[31]

The characteristic cost-saving disposition of the government was evidently a factor in the decision not to put the contract out to tender; as McGilligan noted, 'the result of working it in this unusual fashion has been that the sum of £125,000, consulting engineers' fee, has been definitely saved'.[32] In accordance with the White Paper, Siemens would receive the sum of £10,000 for their project preparation, and then only under certain circumstances (which did not arise).[33]

The government was seeking value for money, and ultimately got it, at Siemens' expense.[34] Contrary to intimations from some quarters, the German companies did not engage in the planning stages of the Shannon Scheme with a view, by unfair means, to excluding competition.[35] Moreover, McGilligan pointed out that it was the only firm who believed in the feasibility of the scheme, and brought it to a stage where it could be implemented.[36]

Large English and US firms did not give serious consideration to Irish electrification prior to Siemens' concrete proposals. In an American enquiry as late as May 1925, the Irish representative in the USA, Professor Smiddy, expressed astonishment that neither General Electric nor Westinghouse nor Stone & Webster had undertaken any action when the Shannon Scheme had first been discussed in 1924.[37] Hurley of Chicago, an influential businessman with excellent connections, was surprised that the Irish government had engaged a Ger-man firm, even though the USA was 'by far the most advanced nation of the world in the field of hydropower utilisation and electricity generation'. He made the suggestion that – if the matter had not advanced too far – the government should speak to the General Electric Co., the 'leading electrical firm in the world', who could successfully execute and finance the Shannon Scheme, especially as the interest of Owen Young, 'Chairman of the Board' of General Electric, and member of the Dawes Expert Commission, would produce a very favourable outcome. However, it is clear that McGilligan strictly rejected approaches from other companies, once the conceptual outlines of the whole venture had been put in place by Siemens.[38]

Although the first presentation by McGilligan on the scheme in December 1924 received a mixed reception in the Dáil, it won the approval of the majority. One of the more positive comments was that of Professor W. Thrift, who expressed the hope that the day would be remembered as one of the greatest in Irish history, in that all attention was concentrated on the most important problems of the country: how Ireland could be brought to a state of prosperity. The potential for this, he claimed, was apparent in the Shannon Scheme plans. Minister McGilligan did not neglect to recall Arthur Griffith, who had so forcefully called for the development of the natural resources of the country.[39] The Shannon Electricity bill was tabled in the Dáil on 1 May 1925 (first stage), and concluded on 26 May 1925 (fifth stage) with the adoption of the bill in the form considered suitable. Following the reading in the Seanad (up to 25 June 1925) it passed into law on 4 July 1925 (Shannon Electricity Act, 1925). Thus another Act was added to those already in existence governing the supply of electricity in the Irish Free State.[40]

With regard to finance, section 11 of the Act directed that a maximum of £5.21 million should be advanced by the Minister for Finance from a central fund, as required, to a special 'Shannon Fund' for the purposes of the scheme. The amounts made available were repayable with interest to the central fund.[41] Section 11 also empowered the Minster for Finance to procure the necessary amounts for the central fund by public loans. This is an indication that it was not intended to finance the Shannon Scheme by taxation.

■ The inclined hoist (next to the power house at Ardnacrusha) in operation.
Source: Siemens Archive, Munich.

The Labour Party (which had taken on the role of opposition) forcefully supported the immediate implementation of the project. Their criticism was essentially constructive. Johnson (the party leader) saw the possibilities offered by the scheme for the decentralization of industry and trade outside the main centres, the resulting relief of population concentration in the big cities, and the raising of living standard and quality of life, especially for inhabitants of rural

■ Work in progress on the 110-kV transmission system.
Source: ESB Archives Photographic Collection.

areas, where Labour had a large support base.[42] A criticism, largely justified in hindsight, was that the Scheme would be detrimental to the Shannon fisheries.[43] The measures taken initially did not ensure the movement of fish through the canal and river bed. These difficulties were overcome to some extent by the erection of a Bor-land-type fish pass, which went into operation from 1959. There were also more general fears about state intervention in the electricity industry.[44] Many saw in this the beginnings of 'state socialism', and the arrival of the great 'Leviathan' described by Hobbes, which would one day swallow up all private rights in Ireland.[45] This concern was not, however, shared by most members.

Some members were simply against awarding the contract to a German firm.[46] However, when these were obviously motivated purely by anglophile sympathies they were met with a vehement response. In particular, the campaign directed against the Shannon Scheme in the British and Irish press was roundly condemned. Cosgrave felt compelled to respond in particular to articles by Senator Griffith,[47] a prominent figure with extensive knowledge and experience in the area of engineering technology.[48] From 1919 he had been for a time President of the British Institution of Civil Engineers, an honour which had never been given to any engineer resident in Ireland.[49] This made it all the more surprising that he allowed himself temporarily to be carried away with severe criticisms of the scheme, and the government's handling of it. His personal interest in harnessing the Liffey goes a long way towards explaining his attitude. A point continually brought forward in the debates was the expected saving in coal consumption. In 1924 coal to a value of £4.17 million was imported into the Free State, and additionally oil to a value of £600,000. Many members expected that the Shannon Scheme would result in a considerable reduction in the bill for imported English coal. The expectations appear, however, to have been over-optimistic, because a much larger portion of coal imports were for industrial and household use. However, the important goal of a high level of independence in electrical energy supply was indeed achieved in the short term. In concluding the debates in the Dáil, the Minister for Finance drew attention to the fact that in addition to the direct effects (supply of cheap electricity for light and power), the psychological effect of the project was of major significance for the future development of the country. The majority of members shared this opinion, and supported the project for this reason. The positive consequences of the electrification of the entire state were summarized: the use of cheap electricity for lighting and power would support and reinforce existing operations in trade, industry and agriculture; it would help establish new industries; it would improve competitiveness and help to decentralize trade and industry and achieve an independent electricity industry; it would reduce unemployment and raise living standards, improving the quality of life of the population, in addition to reducing emigration.[50]

The Dáil debates showed that fears of the negative effects of the scheme were regarded by the government, and by most other members, as incidental compared with the many advantages. The danger to the hydro-works and the overhead lines from potential sabotage had to be taken into account, and the protection of fisheries rights had to take second place. McGilligan stated emphatically that in carrying out this scheme, 'although all reasonable precaution will be taken to prevent injury, we do not preclude the possibility of injury being done to the fisheries, and if in a case of conflict between fishery and electricity interests, then electricity is going to have the superiority'.[51] In relation to the potential threat of bomb attacks on the power plant and the dams, a commentary in *The Irish Statesman* in April 1925 pointed out that if a cautious approach were followed in all cases like this, then none of the constructions needed for civilized human existence, such as reservoirs or aqueducts, could ever be erected.[52]

In the Seanad, where former unionists were particularly strongly represented,[53] a small number of declared opponents of the Shannon Scheme attempted, in the same way as in the Dáil, to obstruct or delay the implementation of the scheme. Here, Senator Sir John Purser Griffith requested that the project be carefully assessed again by a newly formed commission. Griffith anticipated huge technical risks in the construction and operation of the plant and dams. He was also not prepared to believe that the consumption of electrical energy in the Free State would grow in the following years as rapidly as had been projected by the specialists.[54] His principal objection to the project was the fact that the electrification of the entire state would be made dependent on a single large plant.[55]

Another active participant in the Seanad as a critic of the commercial and financial basis of the scheme was Sir John Keane, a director of the Bank of Ireland.[56] He expressed the view that electricity supply in the Irish Free State should progress in a 'natural' way from small beginnings.[57] Keane also made clear that he would have preferred to have the project conducted by British instead of German firms: 'I admit that I should like to see this scheme, other things being equal, given to a British contractor. I am not ashamed of it. I think it is a sound policy to keep your business in the family ... After all, it is common knowledge that the chief customer for our exports is Great Britain.' Keane also complained that the government had not engaged consulting engineers and prepared a specification, and said that if Siemens or any other non-British firm had offered better prices than British firms to such a specification, then for his part he would have nothing against the contract not being given to Great Britain. However, he was clearly not a supporter of the idea of nationalization, referring to the 'poisonous virus of nationalization' and 'the fatal and continuing tendency on the part of the government towards nationalization'.[58]

One of those who criticized the venture, but was interested in the establishment of a project for the utilization of indigenous primary energies as advantageously as possible, was Éamon de Valera, who saw the project as a costly 'white elephant' of limited benefit. His contention was that the planned scheme was too large, and that it would for years tie up considerable capital, which could be better employed elsewhere. He would have preferred to see a beginning made with the smaller Liffey project, which would help train up Irish engineers and craftsmen, who would then be engaged for the execution of the large Shannon project, without the need for people from abroad. He did not, however, persist in his

■ 38 kV switching station in course of construction.
Source: Siemens Archives, Munich.

opposition once the decision had been made to proceed immediately with the Shannon Scheme, and gave his full support to the undertaking.[59]

With the Shannon Electricity Act of 1925, the government of the Irish Free State had established the necessary legislative requirements for a comprehensive electrification programme utilizing hydropower. Yet one major issue remained unresolved: how should electricity be distributed to customers? The government did not intend at the outset that the electricity generated at the Shannon would be delivered on to the consumer by a state undertaking, but by private undertakings and/or local or communal bodies, to whom the electricity would be supplied in bulk. In the course of his visit to America in the autumn of 1925, McGilligan had the opportunity of discussing his interests in this matter with representatives of the electricity industry in the USA and Canada, who at this point began to show a little more interest in the electricity supply of the Irish Free State; various parties enquired if the government would be disposed to award concessions to American undertakings for the implementation of electricity supply.[60]

On 21 January 1926 the Cabinet officially authorized the Minister to contact prominent undertakings, and to establish under what conditions they would be prepared to take over local distribution of electricity, through a consolidated supply company under the control of an Irish supervisory body. Because of the enormous capital requirement, only foreign, particularly American, companies came into consideration. During his stay in the USA and Canada, McGilligan had observed arrangements in some regions which could be applied in an Irish context. He hoped to foster private commercial initiative, and his reservations regarding 'nationalisation' were very clearly expressed in the following extract from his memorandum of December 1925: 'And it is very doubtful whether the national psychology would ultimately benefit if another large addition were made to the present high proportion of citizens who depend on a Government job. An infusion of regulated private enterprise in so important a matter as this should serve as a much-needed tonic for the present apathy.'[61] However, it quickly became apparent that involvement in electricity supply and distribution in the Irish Free State was not sufficiently profitable to the private sector, due to the necessity to supply areas with relatively low levels of consumption. In a memorandum of 15 December 1926, the Minister made clear that a successful outcome could no longer be seriously expected from these negotiations, and that there should be no further delays in the preparation of the necessary legislation and measures for state intervention.

However, there was international opposition to direct state involvement in electricity supply. Among those whose opinion the Irish government could not ignore was one of the most prominent, the Trade Minister (and later President) of the USA, Herbert Hoover. Despite such reservations, the Irish government was obliged to make a major U-turn and to take full control of the supply of electricity to consumers, as the existing supply undertakings in the Free State in 1926, with their 'antiquated business methods', limited supply areas, inefficient and 'rust ridden' plant and distribution systems, lack of standardization and unwillingness to modernize, were simply not a feasible option.[62] Before a final decision was made, a number of foreign electricity supply operations were carefully examined.[63] To a large extent, the organization of the Swedish 'Board of Control' was followed. The government decided to vest the Shannon plant, and all future power stations, together with the transmission and distribution networks up to the consumer, in a 'semi-state' or 'state-sponsored' body to be known as the Electricity Supply Board (ESB), which, in the interests of efficiency, should be protected as far as possible from interference by government. Thus was put in place an organization similar to that which had been used elsewhere with successful results, where management was guided by the model of private enterprise combined with public responsibility. McGilligan also took the view that this solution provided the appropriate training for Irish engineers and other staff.[64] One of the essential differences between the ESB and the organizations that had been studied in other countries was that the final distribution of current to the end consumer would also be in the hands of the organization.[65]

The legislative measures that facilitated the authorization, establishment and efficient operation of the ESB were anchored in the Electricity (Supply) bill, submitted to parliament in 1927. The Electricity (Supply) Act, 1927 came into force on 28 May 1927, and the ESB was brought officially into existence on 11 August 1927.[66] The electricity acts preceding the foundation of the state, i.e. from 1882 to 1919, were repealed,[67] so that only the Shannon Electricity Act, 1925, and the Electricity (Supply) Act, 1927 applied thereafter. The Free State was to become one of the first countries in the world where the state managed the electricity industry, albeit with an element of the spirit of private enterprise.[68]

The following functions were assigned to the ESB under the Electricity (Supply) Act:[69] operation of the Shannon Power Station, transmission and sale of the electrical energy generated; promotion of the use of electrical energy; and control, co-ordination and improvement of electricity supply in the Irish Free State. It is especially noteworthy that the Act of 1927 expressly permitted the ESB itself to manufacture and market electrical machines and appliances, accessories, cables, etc. This was perceived as necessary, since in 1927 there was limited production of such items in the Irish Free State, and products had to be imported from abroad at considerable cost.

The Act in particular made provision for the ESB to acquire electricity supply undertakings already operating in the Irish Free State. 'Authorized' or 'statutory undertakings' up to then in the hands of municipal bodies, such as the Pigeon House steam power station in Dublin, as well as the plants in Rathmines and Pembroke, were taken over at the end of March 1929 without compensation. In the case of the privately owned undertakings, some compensation was paid, and these installations were gradually shut down or integrated into the national grid.[70]

■ Work in the Coffer Dam during Shannon high-water period, 1927.
Source: Siemens Archive, Munich.

The advance to be made available to the ESB for the initial period of its activity was specified in the Electricity (Supply) Act, 1927, as £2.5 million. This was to finance the measures required for an efficient electricity supply, in particular the erection of local distribution networks and connections to consumers and the acquisition of existing electricity undertakings, and to cover maintenance work.[71]

The ESB, under its first Managing Director, McLaughlin, had at the start two main tasks: to take over existing electricity supply undertakings, and to convince a large part of the population within the state of the benefits of electricity in the home, in industry and on the farm, thus establishing the necessary demand to keep the price of Shannon electricity as low as possible. The first of these tasks was complicated by technical problems. Many of the existing small installations operated with direct current. If the consumers connected to these systems were to be supplied with three-phase or single-phase alternating current from the new national grid, the ESB had to decide either to continue to supply these consumers with direct current by conversion from three-phase alternating current, or adapt the direct current distribution system to carry three-phase alternating current. The latter alternative was taken when smaller installations were gradually taken over. The second task was of pressing urgency for the ESB, as completion of the scheme was scheduled for 1929. As there was little experience in the area of marketing, McLaughlin was sent to the USA in order to gain information on measures that could be successfully adopted in Ireland.[72]

For the purposes of informing the public on all the activities of the ESB, a Public Relations Department (and the position of Public Relations Officer) was created on 1 July 1928, following McLaughlin's return. The marketing strategy adopted assumed many forms.[73] Bus trips to the main sites of the Shannon Scheme were organized, and in June 1928 a 'Guide Bureau' was opened. The Great Southern Railways encouraged public visits with greatly reduced fares from all stations to Limerick. Altogether, this information and sightseeing campaign, complemented by advertisements in all major national newspapers and magazines, was a huge success.[74] In the period from June 1928 to March 1932, 185,000 sightseers (or roughly 6 per cent of the total population of the Irish Free State) visited Ardnacrusha.[75] In addition, the ESB produced brochures and posters, set up showrooms and shops for electrical equipment, and conducted information presentations and slide-shows even in the smallest locations. A film was made about the scheme,[76] and at the request of the ESB, Siemens constructed a model of the power station, which was displayed from May 1929 at exhibitions throughout the Irish Free State, attracting large crowds.[77]

But it was not possible in the beginning to offer electricity supply to every home in the state. At first, only locations with at least 500 inhabitants were connected to the expanding national grid. Smaller villages, and single houses and farmsteads, could initially only be connected if they were not too far from the lines of the network, and the load was large enough to produce an acceptable cost-benefit. The others had to do without electricity for the time being, unless they were being supplied by one of the small supply undertakings that were gradually taken over by the ESB. The exclusion of a part of the population from electricity supply at that time was unavoidable on economic grounds, even though, in the early years following commissioning of the Shannon power station, a considerable surplus of energy was available, particularly during periods of high rainfall.

The comprehensive electrification of the Irish Free State greatly expanded the market for electro-technical products. As there were no effective manufacturers for these products in Ireland, a favourable market was opened for foreign firms. For the German electrical industry, also, the Irish market became of more interest from the middle of the 1920s. Siemens opened a subsidiary in Dublin for electrical products, Siemens-Schuckert (Ireland) Ltd, at the beginning of 1925.[78] The Shannon Scheme and the construction of the national grid, and the connection of consumers, were of major importance in reducing the high level of unemployment in the country. Apart from the fact that many thousands found work on the Shannon Scheme, the ESB had in the following years employed a large number of workers, engineers and clerks for the operation of power stations, for load distribution centres, the maintenance and expansion of the national grid, and for domestic installations, consumer advice, planning of further plants and the training of new recruits, etc.[79] The loss of employment resulting from the closing of existing small supply undertakings and rationalization within the ESB was more than offset by the creation of new opportunities. Training in the Free State in the field of electro-technology was considerably enhanced and qualitatively improved by the facilities within the ESB.

It is evident therefore that there was a significant change in attitude towards the potential involvement of the public sector in developing Ireland's electricity industry in the period between 1922 and 1927, despite the ideological opposition to such a course of action at the outset. This was not because of any dramatic ideological transformation within the government in the interim period, but as a result of the circumstances facing the government when private-sector companies were unwilling to invest in distributing electricity throughout the state. The Shannon Scheme had begun before the decision was made to set up a semi-state body to organize the electricity supply to consumers. McGilligan (who had initially supported private investment as the way forward in establishing the distribution network) was forced to change his approach when it became apparent that no private investment was forthcoming, due to the low profits expected from supplying large areas with low demand. Essentially the scale of the scheme forced the government to establish an organization to distribute electricity nationally. This entailed far greater involvement by the state in all aspects of the electricity industry than it had anticipated, and more than had been the case in any other country up to this point. It was a highly radical measure for a conservative government to embark upon. One of the historians of the ESB concluded: 'Never before or since has an Irish government taken such a calculated risk and never before had a single economic project assumed such importance as a fundamental act of nation-building.'[80]

How the Shannon Scheme Workers Lived

Michael McCarthy

In 1925 the townland of Ballykeelaun in south-east Clare, about three miles from Limerick city, took on the appearance of an Irish Klondyke. From every corner of the country, and even from Scotland, men converged on the little village of Ardnacrusha in the hope of securing one of the 3000 jobs on the Shannon Scheme. The people of the village found themselves swamped by thousands of navvies who were 'housed' in nearby huts, stables, hen-houses, pigsties and barns.

The Shannon Electricity bill became law in June 1925. On 13 August the contract between the Free State government and the German company of Siemens-Schuckert was signed. The contract was to cost £5.2 million and was to be completed within three and a half years.[1] Within days of the contract being signed, engineers had arrived from Germany and work on the scheme got under-way.[2] Sites were pegged out and routes prepared for 62 miles of railway track, hundreds of trucks, locomotives, cranes, stone-crushers, diggers and other heavy machinery soon to be imported from Hamburg. The stretch of farmland between O'Brien's Bridge, just below Killaloe, and Longpavement, near Limerick city, a distance of about six or seven miles, was transformed into a massive building site. For those who were out of work or even for those employed as farm labourers, the prospect of a job on the Shannon Scheme looked very attractive.

■ A diver takes a well-earned break.
Source: ESB Archives Photographic Collection.

In September an advertisement appeared in the national press for 3000 unskilled workers for construction work on the Shannon river area in counties Limerick and Clare. Wages were set at thirty-two shillings a week for a fifty-hour week with free lodgings. The advertisement also stated that canteens were to be established and run by Irish contractors, where cooked food and other necessities could be bought for cost price. Applicants were requested to fill in the printed form and address it to 'The Shannon Scheme, Dublin.' Siemens' Irish headquarters were located at 43 Upper O'Connell Street, which had been the offices of the National Land League. The unions reacted angrily to the wages and conditions as advertised in the press.[3] A bitter and protracted strike ensued, as workers demanded that the level of remuneration should be at a level appropriate for a great national project, under the auspices of the government. Dr McLoughlin, Siemens' representative in Ireland, entered the controversy on 28 September. He claimed that the rate being offered compared favourably with the going rates for agricultural labourers, and it was these, not city labourers, who should be used as the proper basis for comparison. The average agricultural wage at the time was 25/- for a 57–60-hour week.[4] *The Voice of Labour* was quick to reply that it was unfair to compare the Shannon Scheme labourer to the farm labourer, who often received some extra benefits in kind over and above the 32/- a week. It blamed McGilligan, the Minister for Industry and Commerce, for signing the contract without the advice of the trade union movement. 'It was signed as if the working class had no rights, no authority, no recognised status in the State. The Minister had acted in the spirit of an age before the repeal of the Anti-Combination Acts in 1824.'[5]

On 30 September Joseph McGrath, the former Minister for Industry and Commerce, was appointed Director of Labour for Siemens-Schuckert. His

■ Timber work at intake building.
Source: ESB Archives Photographic Collection.

appointment dismayed the unions. McGrath had been an organizer with Larkin's union, the Workers Union of Ireland in Dublin, and later had been head of the Irish Secret Service; he was thus able to provide the company with useful information as a result of his previous association with both the government and the trade-union movement. At the time of his appointment as Director of Labour for Siemens he had been out of work and in financial difficulties, having resigned from the Dáil some months previously. On the day of his appointment McGrath opened negotiations with the Transport Union. No agreement was reached.[6] McGrath, however, was determined to resolve the dispute and he quickly approached another branch of ex-servicemen's associations, unaffiliated to the Transport Union, with an offer of 50/- a week; this was accepted. Gradually he wore down the strikers and by Christmas the dispute was over. After that it was left to the wags to sing about it in the pubs, which they did.

> Thirty-two bob! Thirty-two bob!
> Come and we'll give you a beautiful job!
> Come and enjoy some light recreation

Down on the Shannon electrification!
Sit down at once and send in your name,
And start playing an elegant game;
All you've to do is spend a few hours
Admiring the sun as it shines through the showers,
While you're up to your waist in mud and in stink,
Wielding a shovel or staking quick lime,
Shoving a barrow or lifting a load,
Digging a channel or making a road,
We don't want to strain you,
And so we won't detain you
For more than fifty hours on the job,
And for that we'll pay you thirty-two bob![7]

Apart from the occasional strains of this ballad from the pubs of Limerick, little enough was heard of the industrial dispute after that.

By mid-June 1926 the public mind once more was focused on south-east Clare as newspapers alleged that workers on the Shannon Scheme were living in barns, stables and pigsties, and called for a special inquiry. The ferment of ingredients for this latest controversy had been bubbling away for months. Employment on the works had risen rapidly to over 2000 since major construction had begun in September 1925.[8] Maximum sleeping accommodation for the Irish workers, skilled and unskilled, at Ardnacrusha camp was 720 and that was only achieved in 1928, by which time employment had risen to 5000.[9] In 1926 approximately 1300 had to find accommodation either in Limerick city or in the neighbourhood of the works. Meanwhile, scores of men walked to Ardnacrusha from all parts of Ireland looking for a job; some were sent by their local Labour Exchange, others went with nothing but hope.[10] There was no dole in those days, and alternative employment prospects were limited.

For less than a quarter of the 2000-odd employed on the Shannon Scheme in June 1926, free sleeping accommodation was available in the site camp in one of the timber huts provided by the contractors.[11] For the rest, local lodgings could cost anything from 2/- to £1 a week.[12] Meals could be bought in the camp canteen at the reduced rate of 11/8 a week.[13] A pint of porter cost 6 pence. Health and unemployment insurance deductions amounted to 1/1 a week.[14] A visit to Limerick's Coliseum or Grand Central to see the latest silent Tom Mix or Gary Cooper film would cost 1/- or 1/6.[15] So, for those lucky enough to get jobs the financial pressure of having to provide their own accommodation was considerable, particularly if they were married and had hoped to send home something to their wives and children. The less fortunate were confronted by two options: the long dusty road home or just hanging about in the hope that the following morning might bring a job for them. In the meantime, they had to find somewhere to sleep.

■ Street in the Irish camp.
Source: Siemens, Progress on the Shannon, Number 4, January 1927.

One of the most obvious places for those without work to look for accommodation was in the City Home in Limerick. During April, May and the beginning of June 1926, an average of ten people, unable to find work on the Shannon Scheme, were admitted each night. Towards the end of June, the number seeking admission had dropped to five a night. But then the City Health Board refused admittance to all those coming from outside the Borough of Limerick.[16] This decision was related to a question that had been occupying the minds of the Clare County Board of Health and the Limerick City Home and Hospital Committee for some months, namely: who was responsible for the medical care of the Shannon Scheme workers?[17] The German contractors refused to hold themselves responsible, stating that their liability ceased when they complied with the terms of the National Health and Unemployment Acts. Clare County Board of Health held that, even though the Shannon Scheme was situated in Clare, the county's hospitals could not cope. It argued that Scarriff District Hospital had only two beds for those who were not natives of Clare; that the Fever Hospital in Ennis, with only twenty beds, catering for east, central and north Clare, was already inadequate for current needs; and that the County Hospital in Ennis, being the County Home, held a certain number of beds for the poor of the county but had no extra beds available for the Shannon Scheme workers. Limerick Board of Health argued in similar vein that it was incapable of meeting the needs of the Shannon Scheme and that the Minister for Industry and Commerce should make the contractors responsible for the provision of adequate housing for the workforce.[18] In fact, there was a medical officer at Ardnacrusha and a few beds for the injured and sick. But these facilities were entirely inadequate to deal with thousands of unskilled men working under pressure with heavy machinery and explosives.

■ Krupp tipping-wagon. *Source: Siemens, Progress on the Shannon, Number 6, March 1927.*

It was on Thursday, 24 June, at one of its regular monthly meetings, that the Clare County Board of Health first heard of Shannon Scheme workers sleeping in pigsties and stables.[19] The Board had just listened to a report from its Secretary, John Quinn, on a conference between the Limerick and Clare County Boards and the Department of Local Government on the subject of treating the sick and injured of the Shannon Scheme. The conference had requested the Minister for Local Government to introduce in the Dáil a bill that would allow the transfer to their homes of workers from other counties or countries, in the event of their being destitute, sick or injured. The representative of the Department had told the conference that Clare and Limerick County Boards of Health could refuse relief to any man coming from outside their respective areas. The report on the conference was warmly welcomed by the members of the Clare Board. As a post-script to its meeting, the Home Assistance Officer (H.A.O.) for Ardnacrusha was asked for a brief report on the latest position in the area. H.A.O. Mullane stated that a large number of workers had billeted themselves in stables, cowsheds and barns. There was, he said, no hut accommodation for many of them. He reported that a man and his wife had taken possession of a pigsty attached to a labourer's cottage, and there were no fewer than twelve to fourteen workers in a

■ Charging the bore holes.
Source: Siemens, Progress on the Shannon, Number 6, March 1928.

stable at Blackwater in O'Grady's yard. Some of these men were unemployed and some were not. The H.A.O. informed the Board that about 400 workers were being laid off within a few days and he wanted to know what he would do with those who remained in his district and became destitute. There was, he said, a constant procession through eight miles of his district by men looking for work or going home after failing to get work.[20]

■ Concrete work
for power house.
Source: ESB Archives
Photographic Collection.

A spirited debate followed. Councillor McMahon of Blackwater corroborated the statement of the H.A.O. that people were living in pigsties and that some men (and their wives) remained on in the district after being dismissed from the Shannon Scheme. 'Surely to God', he exclaimed, 'we are not going to let them die with the hunger'. Councillor Halpin was of the opinion that the government should shoulder its responsibility to save people from living like 'mere swine'. This view was echoed by other members of the Board. Councillor Halpin also cited the case of a man lying in a pigsty with straw for a bed whilst he was suffering from double pneumonia. Councillor Crowe asked: 'Are we to feed the hungry of every county in Ireland?' Councillor McMahon replied: 'We would and divide our last penny with the poor, but if we have not a penny, what then?' The Board resolved that it would abide by the principle of the inter-county conference and grant relief only to Claremen. It also ordered a comprehensive report on conditions in and around Ardnacrusha from the Medical Inspector of Health for the area, Dr Enright.

Two days after the County Board of Health meeting, the national press had picked up the story of housing conditions on the Shannon Scheme.[21] The *Irish Independent* recorded the Home Assistance Officer's statements at the Board of Health meeting on its editorial page under the heading 'A Very Amazing Story'. Three days later the story had been moved to the world news page and a call was made for a special inquiry and for an early remedy for the inadequate housing conditions of the Shannon Scheme workers. The newspaper had also made its own investigation and published an exclusive report which corroborated the statements of H.A.O. Mullane. Referring to the pigsty attached to the labourer's cottage, the report stated:

> The latter accommodates a husband, a wife and two children. Some of the places in which men are sleeping are not at all fit for human beings. There was one place referred to by the Home Assistance Officer. It was merely an out-office; it might have housed horses or cattle. The beds consisted of old hay, thrown on the floor, with no suggestion of bed clothing. One of the heaps of hay was semi-covered with an old sack. This was the very place in which 15 men slept up to a short time ago. The number has now dwindled down to eight and those men are paying rent for the privilege of accommodation. They are being charged 2/- a week for the shelter of the roof and the bed of hay self-provided. ... The Camp Commandant at Ardnacrusha, Mr. W.J. Stapleton, when interviewed on the matter, stated that it was possible that there were men living in outhouses, but they were not employed on the Scheme and that it was not because of lack of accommodation. 'This morning there were only two men on my waiting list for beds,' he said. He further explained to me that some months ago before the huts were completed there was not sufficient accommodation, and the men were obliged to fend for themselves and do the best they could; but now they were able to cater for them. He went on to say that when hut accommodation was not available, the fact was stated to the men before they were employed, and as a result of the rapidly approaching completion of the temporary works at Ardnacrusha, between 200 and 300 men had been disemployed during the past month, and whilst an effort was being made to give them at least one night's accommodation after dismissal, they could not be held responsible for them afterwards.

A further matter which he pointed out was that men were arriving at the works daily from all parts of the country, oftimes penniless, seeking to find employment and unable to find any. It was quite conceivable that those men in numerous instances were obliged to sleep out.

The report also called for an impartial inquiry into housing conditions for the workers.[22]

One would imagine that at that stage the unions would have become involved in a campaign to improve living conditions and would have used it as a platform to raise the general lot of Irish workers on the Scheme. Unfortunately there is little evidence to suggest that this was the case. A meeting had been held in Ardnacrusha on Sunday, 17 April, which was addressed by Cathal O'Shannon and Paddy Hogan, TD, who supported a move to organize the unskilled workers and to get them into the Irish Transport and General Workers' Union; a resolution to this effect was adopted.[23] That was the last reported union meeting on the Shannon Scheme and the last indication of any union activity for the remainder of the contract.[24]

Even the *Voice of Labour*, which had played such an important role in the Shannon Scheme strike six months earlier by its uncompromising stand and reportage, showed only a short-lived interest. On 3 July it gave front-page coverage to the situation at Ardnacrusha.[25] Under the heading 'Not Fit For Human Beings' it stated that the revelations of the correspondent of the *Irish Independent* may have been amazing to the capitalist press but not to the *Voice of Labour*. Another edition carried an angry letter signed by 'Man from Nowhere'. The writer stated that he had seen worse slavery in Mexico. He decried the working conditions – the bread, tea and margarine for breakfast; the extra cup of tea for two pence and the extra slice of bread for one penny. He quoted a worker as saying: 'We are working for our chuck, and slowly starving to death on it.' Having condemned the bullying German and Irish bosses, the writer declared: 'What is the labour movement, the republican movement and the Church doing to expose and do away with this infamy? I would warn all three to be up and doing, particularly the latter, as their silence is roundly condemned by the workers in the huts after their day of slavery.'

That letter was followed by another signed by 'A worker on the job', who wrote:

> The conditions on the Shannon Scheme cannot, I will venture to say, have any parallel in Europe at present. Take, for instance, the wages of 8 pence an hour with broken time – and God knows for some weeks we get lots of that. Most of the men are in debt every weekend, and I may add if they were to eat enough of good plain food working as navvies shovelling concrete, or up to their knees in water attending the diggers down below, the wages of even the full week which amount to 34/-, would not be sufficient to buy sustaining food for a hard-working navvy. I have seen my countrymen housed in the cowsheds of England and Scotland years ago. There, at least, the sheds were fairly warm and sanitary compared to the sheds of the farmers of Blackwater where my countrymen are housed now and pay 18/- a week for a half-roofed shed. …
>
> Let your Labour members ask Mr. McGilligan why are three or four hundred men per week sent from labour exchanges to the job, and a similar number sacked after from one to six weeks' work and left to drift back home, and sacked for no cause. Ask McGilligan why it was a man was crushed to death between two wagons when the Irish foreman told him not to go on the wagon as it was dangerous. The German told him to get up or go. His son gave evidence to this effect and was immediately dismissed. Ask him why the Camp Commandant Stapleton will pull down a notice the men put up, and tell them 'they must not talk of a union here'. Ask him why it is that when the men put up a lean-to for the purpose of cooking, because their wages won't buy them sufficient food in the canteen, it's pulled down.
>
> Last week the workers had one holiday and two wet days. No money to buy food this week. Yet another holiday today, Thursday! We would advise the workers to get busy and give them the following advice:
>
> > 'Quit hollering out for martyrs
> > To be slaughtered in your sight;
> > Get off your knees, you lobsters
> > And learn to think and fight!'[26]

The apparent disengagement by the unions, following so rapidly on the heels

■ Installation of equipment in turbine hall.
Source: ESB Archives Photographic Collection.

of the strike, which had held up work on the Scheme for months, may have been because at this point the unions were demoralized. McGrath had out-flanked and out-played the unions during the strike by hiring ex-servicemen from the Free State army, including a captain as camp commandant, while excluding would-be troublemakers and union organizers.[27] The contractors also, reportedly, encouraged the formation of bogus unions in the Ardnacrusha camp, set up an effective camp-informer network, and employed a 'heavy gang' to enforce law and order.[28]

The housing conditions in Ardnacrusha were debated in the Dáil on 1 July. McGilligan, the Minister for Industry and Commerce, was asked by Deputy Lyons (Longford-Westmeath) whether reports that appeared in the press as to the manner in which men worked on the Shannon Scheme were correct? The Minister replied: 'You may take it *prima facie* that the press is inaccurate.'[29] But the Munster deputies were not to be as easily dismissed. Later in the afternoon

■ Installation of turbines.
*Source: ESB Archives
Photographic Collection.*

Deputy Hogan, the Minister for Agriculture, in whose constituency the Shannon Scheme was based, gave notice that on the motion for the adjournment he would raise the question of the shortage of accommodation for the care of the workers on the Scheme when they were sick or injured. McGilligan tried to head this off by stating that there was accommodation in the camp for 140 more men than were there at that point in time. But Hogan was not to be dissuaded and repeated his intention of raising the question of accommodation during the adjournment debate. In this, he cited the example of

> a worker from Co. Mayo who has been unemployed, say, for a period of twelve months, or, perhaps two years, and has therefore lapsed in National Health Insurance. … He gets work on the Shannon Scheme and after two or three months he becomes ill or injured. He has eight or twelve National Health Insurance stamps, probably, to his credit and he has no claim upon the funds of any National Health Insurance Society. He has to fall back on the arrangements made by the local health authorities of the district, while the local health authorities have only made arrangements to meet normal conditions.[30]

Hogan argued that since the Shannon Scheme was an exceptional case, and since the local health authorities were unable to cope with the situation, the

Minister should make special provision for the workers. He then got on to the question of general accommodation. 'I would like to say that I am not very much interested in the opinions expressed by the Minister in the press report – the opinion expressed by him this afternoon in reply to questions addressed to him by Deputy Lyons.'[31] He quoted from the report of H.A.O. Mullane to the Clare County Board of Health and from the minutes of the County Board meeting where H.A.O. Mullane was complimented by the Chairman of the County Board 'on his report as to the extraordinary circumstances in which people were living – in outhouses, pig-sties and barns and lying on straw'. From information he had received from public officials in the Ardnacrusha area he supported the veracity of the H.A.O.'s report and called on the Minister to state what arrangements he had made regarding the sick and injured and in regard to accommodation in general. Hogan was supported by Deputy Clancy from Limerick:

> If something is not done very soon as regards the sanitary arrangements at Ardnacrusha, I greatly fear that an epidemic will break out that will be more serious than the 'flu epidemic we had in this country in 1918 and 1919. I was there in the months of April and May, and I must say that the air was anything but pleasant … if that condition of affairs is allowed to continue, I think that the people of Limerick and Clare will very soon have to turn their noses towards the Government and appeal to have something done.[32]

The Minister for Industry and Commerce replied to both speakers with what could be described as a typical McGilligan broadside. 'I put in direct negation to what Deputy Clancy has said that there is a medical officer in the camp, and that the sanitary arrangements at Ardnacrusha are as sound as they could be on any works. As far as these arrangements are concerned, there is not the slightest fear of any attack or any epidemic such as the Deputy has outlined here tonight.'[33] As for Hogan's arguments, the Minister did not deal with them directly, but made a personal attack on H.A.O. Mullane. 'We have the statements made by his Home Assistance Officer who strangely enough put in some very hard work indeed for a fortnight before he issued his report trying to get a son or a relative employed on the scheme under these filthy conditions that he has described. The bad sanitary arrangements and the other matters that he refers to would appear to have only been discovered when he could not procure a post for his relative under the scheme.'[34] The Minister then insisted that it would be outrageous to expect the contractors to provide hospital beds for all the sick and injured. There were a few beds in the camp for accident cases and it was up to the Clare and Limerick authorities to look after the rest, he said.

The debate went on until after 10 p.m., with McGilligan not giving an inch. In conclusion, Deputy Murphy (of West Cork) asked: 'Has the Minister any statement to make with regard to the report that appeared in the *Irish Independent*, on the conditions, from a journalist who was sent specially to investigate matters?'[35] McGilligan replied, 'I saw the statement there of the Commandant of the camp which, I think, answered the journalist's statement perfectly.'[36] The Dáil adjourned at 10.25 p.m. On the following day the *Irish Times* reported the Dáil debate and the next issue of the *Limerick Leader* also carried a parliamentary report, but it was left to the *Clare Champion* to defend its countrymen in the face of the Minister's attack.[37] McGilligan had accompanied President Cos-grave to a Cumann na nGaedheal convention in Limerick City Hall on 10 July. During their visit they took time off to tour the works at Ardnacrusha and to inspect the accommodation. At the convention the Minister was attacked for his statements in the Dáil on living conditions at Ardnacrusha and his arguments were flatly rebutted.[38] Seemingly the experience at the convention chastened McGilligan somewhat. The next issue of the *Clare Champion* reported:

> During his recent visit to Limerick the Minister for Industry and Commerce seems to have been convinced that a number of workers employed on the Shannon Scheme were living in outhouses in the neighbourhood of Ardnacrusha under insanitary conditions, and he admitted that the Boards of Health of Limerick and Clare in drawing attention to them were not activated by unworthy motives. Mr McGilligan would have done the gracious act if he had also withdrawn his suggestion that Home Assistance Officer Mullane reported the conditions merely because a relative had not got a job on the works. Mr Mullane reported the conditions in the ordinary course of his duty. In his official capacity, Mr Mullane would have been blameworthy if he had allowed men to crowd into barns and stables without remark. There was no suggestion that the Shannon Scheme contractors were responsible for the actions of the men,

and no slur was cast upon the manner in which the works are being conducted. But when men herd in stables and pig sties, there is an obvious menace to the public health, and if timely measures were not taken to deal with it the consequences might be very grave.[39]

The Medical Inspector of Health for Ardnacrusha, Dr Enright, visited the area on 5 July. He presented his report on accommodation during the same week to a meeting of the Clare County Board of Health.[40] He found that seven houses in which workers lodged – Henneberry, Haskins, Lavery, Greensmith, Leahy, Ryan and Hogan – were satisfactory. An eighth house was somewhat congested, in a ruined building on Hartigan's land, in which eleven men lived and slept on shavings. Dr Enright found conditions there unsatisfactory. In O'Grady's yard there were eight or ten occupants living under insanitary conditions. In a sty attached to Keegan's labourer's cottage there was a husband, a wife and two children living under insanitary conditions. All of the men living in those places, with one exception, were working on the Shannon Scheme. Dr Enright also reported that a number of independent traders had opened shops in the district. They were all very clean inside, but the outside sanitary arrangements were defective. As to hut accommodation at the works, Dr Enright said the average number in each hut was twenty-six.

■ Living-room in Irish camp.
Source: Siemens Progress on the Shannon, Number 4, January 1927.

A discussion of the report followed. Mr Kerin, Chairman of the Board, said that Dr Enright's report refuted the Minister's remark in the Dáil and corroborated the report of Home Assistance Officer Mullane. Mr McMahon stated that the man in the pigsty was earning 1/- an hour and so could not afford to stay in the huts himself and pay for his wife and children's accommodation elsewhere. An order was made to close the ruin on Hartigan's land and the stable at O'Grady's yard, while a directive was also given that the sty attached to the labourer's cottage should not be sublet. The Chairman closed the meeting with the general observation that 'the Poor Law was never intended to meet an emergency of this kind, and the Government and the contractors should shoulder their responsibilities'.[41]

■ General view of construction from headrace.
Source: ESB Archives Photographic Collection.

In November 1925 the government had acquired through compulsory order Hartigan's farm at Ardnacrusha for use as part of the Scheme. Hartigan, of Quinville House, Parteen, like most of the other farmers and landowners in the district, had not yet been compensated for his loss of land. So when the order came from the Clare County Board of Health to close up the buildings on the farm he reacted swiftly and angrily. He wrote to the Board: 'The Germans took that farm from me last November. They took the stones out of the doors and windows and converted them to their own use. It is bad enough to have my own land gone and no sign of getting paid for it without being compelled to look after it.'[42] Hartigan's complaint was minor in comparison with the anomaly, as pointed out by a justice in the Civil Bill Court in Limerick in 1928, whereby one government department was taking land without paying compensation and another government department was suing for land annuities.[43]

The constant pressure from the officers of the Clare County Board of Health seems to have eliminated the worst of the accommodation abuses at Ardnacrusha, temporarily at least. Where the occupants of the stables and pigsties went for accommodation is uncertain, but perhaps a clue is provided by the *Limerick Leader* of 6 October. The Clare County Board had been discussing the illegal erection of thirteen huts on plots tenanted by locals.[44] When called on by the County Board to explain why they had allowed huts to be erected on public property, one tenant wrote: 'I wish to inform you that my plot is of no value owing to the work in progress on the Shannon Scheme being carried out in the vicinity. The only way out of the situation was to sublet it to a few friends who have given me a small fee for the use of the huts for a few months. Only for so doing myself and my family would be on the verge of starvation …'[45] Another tenant explained his position: 'I wish to inform you that my plot was of no value to me owing to the work carried on here. I could sow nothing in the plot as it was encroached upon by every form of trespass. The only thing left me to do was to oblige a few who helped me by giving me a small item for the place for a few huts for a few months.'[46] Members of the County Board of Health noted the correspondence, and they also noted that employment on the Scheme was over 3000; they decided to take no action against the tenants and to leave the illegal huts.[47]

The New Year of 1928 brought echoes of the housing scandal of 1926, and worse. The first week of February saw the *Clare Champion* with the front page headline, 'Crowds in Stable – Shocking Conditions at Ardnacrusha'. Dr Enright had reported to the Clare County Board of Health that housing problems had again arisen in the Shannon Scheme area. O'Grady's yard in Blackwater was singled out by the Medical Officer as the main place requiring the attention of the County Engineer's office. In the past year O'Grady's yard had been occupied for a time by workers before they were evacuated by officers of the Board of Health. This time, workers, their wives and children constituted the 'households' in the crowded stables and outhouses of O'Grady's yard.[48] Dr Enright listed the families, ninety-four people in all. In the Hogan family he reported that the husband had been moved to hospital suffering from typhoid fever, having been admitted on

the certificate of Dr McSweeney. He pointed out that the typhoid case shows that 'the drainage requires immediate attention whilst the list of families resident in the place makes it obvious that the area is very congested'.[49] It is believed the occupants of the stables and outhouses were being charged £1 a week.

The next meeting of the County Board of Health took place on 9 February 1928. A letter from the Department of Local Government was read acknowledging receipt of Dr Enright's report. The department 'presumed that the Board of Health will obtain further information from the Medical Officer of Health as to the character of the housing accommodation, whether the congestion is due to circumstances of a permanent or temporary nature and what remedial measures are available, and will then proceed to consider the advisability of dealing with the situation so disclosed under the powers conferred on them by the Public Health Acts'.[50] This piece of bureaucratic jargon returned the ball to the County Board's court and effectively forced the Board to close down O'Grady's yard once again. Nothing more was heard of housing conditions on the Shannon Scheme, even though employment rose at one stage to over 5000, putting extreme pressure on whatever accommodation was available.[51] In general, like the bitterly fought issue of labourers' wages which threatened the scheme in 1925, the issue of living conditions for the workers, as a platform for change in the new state, was gradually vacated by public representatives and politicians. Organized labour had passed up an opportunity to put its own stamp on the biggest industrial undertaking since independence.

There is no doubt that Paddy McGilligan could have put more pressure on the German contractors to improve the lot of Irish workers. He argued publicly, at all times, that it would be unfair and unreasonable to expect the Germans to carry any more responsibility than they already bore. No doubt he also had a fear of cost overruns, which were realized at the end of the Scheme, at Siemens' and the government's expense. McGilligan's approach was fully consistent with the stringent fiscal regime of the most tight-fisted government in the history of the state. The Germans, in fact, cannot really be faulted because, as is now known, they were quite prepared to pay more and to raise the standard of accommodation. McGilligan's inflexibility in the face of these protracted disputes, inevitably made him the object of criticism and satire; the following was published in *Voice of Labour*:

I am McGilligan, McGilligan, McGilligan!
Never shall you see such wonderful skill again.
I've got a plan on
Down where the Shannon
Rolls to the foaming sea.
Jealous folks say it is a bit of a gamble
But we know better, don't we?
For there's Siemens-Schuckert and Gordon Campbell,
Joe McGrath and McLaughlin and me!

So now come all ye unemployed,
You surely should be overjoyed,
At the finest job that was ever seen,
Thirty-two bob and a cheap canteen;
We want every man on,
So come to the Shannon
Come down to the Shannon with me.
I'm McGilligan, McGilligan, McGilligan!
See me bend resistance to my will again
From Derry I came
To the Halls of Fame
Like a blast from the North

My decree has gone forth,
And as I have told you before
There is thirty-two bob
For each man on the job
And never a half-penny more.
They say it's outrageous
But I say it's courageous
To pay to a navvy agricultural wages;
Anyway there's a job
At thirty-two bob
Ready to begin
With the food thrown in.
So don't mind the ban on
Come on to the Shannon
Come down to the Shannon with me.

Chorus
Dot vos McGilligan, McGilligan, McGilligan.
He will our empty pouches fill again;
Ja! Ja! Ja!
Ja! Ja! Ja!
Qui! Qui! Qui!
C'est comme ca.
Dot vos von
Great big man
Ja!
Ja!
Ja!
McGilligan.[52]

With the presence of so many men in a small area, most of them living under dire conditions, it was inevitable that crime levels would increase. One district justice commented that the locality had become very troublesome. The government drew up elaborate defence plans to counter would-be saboteurs, but these never had to be implemented.[53] Most of the crime associated with the Scheme was of a petty nature and much of it resulted from the economic conditions under which men lived and worked. For example, some armed and masked employees on the Scheme held up the mail motor-car at Kilmore, Broadford, in November 1927, robbing £100 – and the car, which they later abandoned at Hassett's Cross, Meelick. Subsequently they were captured and brought to trial.[54] Some appearances in court were the direct result of the economic conditions under which the workers lived. Daniel Flynn of Tipperary, a labourer at Ardnacrusha, was brought before Justice Troy at Tipperary District Court by the Great Southern Railways for travelling from Oola to Limerick on 10 October 1927 without a ticket. He explained to the court that working on the Scheme he did not earn enough to buy a ticket, worth 2/8. He made £1 for a three-day week in bad weather. He sent 5/- a week to his mother. After paying for his digs he had nothing left. He was given a 5/- fine with 20/- costs.[55] While theft of food, clothes, bicycles and tools was by far the most common crime on the scheme, occasionally it took more serious proportions. For example, in November 1928, John Hogan, John O'Neill and Ed Toomey appeared in Ennis District Court for attempting to rob £2,000 from the pay office at Ardtaggle, O'Brien's Bridge. The robbery had been planned in the disused Blackwater Mill but the gang was captured by Gardaí before they had completed the job.[56]

■ Wooden houses for married German employees. *Source: Siemens, Progress on the Shannon, Number 4, January 1927.*

With 500 Germans largely controlling an Irish labour force it was inevitable that racial friction would occasionally make the courts, but not as often as one might expect. There was the case of German foremen being assaulted by Irish navvies and of guards being attacked by razor-wielding Germans, but none demonstrated the anomalies of the situation better than a case in Killaloe

■ Working on the penstocks.
Source: ESB Archives Photographic Collection.

District Court on 21 April 1928. It concerned three Germans, one charged with drunkenness and the other two with falsely representing themselves as bona fide travellers. Only one admitted to having 'a leedle English' but managed to translate for the other two. The justice asked if the summonses were translated into German before being served. Superintendent Mooney replied that all aliens were supposed to know either Irish or English once they were admitted to the Free State and that they had to sign their names either in Irish or English on admission. The gentleman charged with being drunk seemed to have difficulty in following proceedings and kept repeating 'trunkenheit', 'nein'. But when the judge fined him 5/- he produced two half-crowns without the slightest hint from the amateur interpreter.[57]

But language was a problem for not only the Germans. The men from West Galway and from the Aran Islands stuck very much to themselves on the scheme and conducted their business through Irish. The first Connemara man on the Shannon Scheme to be brought to court was Edward O'Loughlin, who was charged with stealing 30/- from another workman and for assaulting him. The judge commented that he was the first Irish-speaker to come before him and asked the Garda to translate. O'Loughlin was fined £4 for stealing and 5/- for assault.[58] The fact that the Connemara men did not mix much with men from other counties and that they did not speak English made them the butt of many jokes. Eventually the men from the West got tired of being ridiculed. On Sunday night, 4 September 1927, led by John MacDonagh of Lettermore, about forty of them went on the rampage in Clonlara.[59] A bottle was sent flying through a window and that signalled the start of proceedings. The MacDonagh brothers, the Flahertys and the Mannions, armed with sticks, stones and other missiles, attacked the occupants of other huts. They smashed everything before them and when the dust settled two people had to be hospitalized, a large number were treated for minor injuries and there were fourteen arrests. It was only with the help of the Gardaí from O'Brien's Bridge that the Clonlara police eventually restored order. That night the fourteen men were brought to Limerick County jail in an open truck. Subsequently in the District Court evidence was given by the other workers against the attackers to the effect that the Connemara men did a lot of overtime, which caused jealousy, that they were looked on as uncivilized for their lack of English, and that they were an unwashed, dirty lot. Both MacDonaghs were fined £2 and the others were fined £1 each for causing bodily injury and damage to property.[60]

Just two months before the official opening of the Scheme one of its saddest and tragic chapters was closed: a former employee was hanged for murder. On Friday, 21 December 1928, a Bavarian foreman, Jacob Kunz of Ardnacrusha, was struck by an assailant with an iron bar at Parteen-a-lax while returning from Limerick. He died a short time afterwards. John Cox, an ex-soldier from Limerick who had formerly worked with Kunz, was later charged with the murder and robbery of £80-10-0 from the Bavarian's pocket and of £409-10-0 which he had sewn on his vest.[61] The accused was charged in Limerick District Court on Saturday, 29 December, and was remanded until 15 January 1929. In the meantime the money was found under a stone in Corbally. The case was heard in Dublin Central Court on 11 March. After four days the jury found him guilty and he was sentenced to hang on 11 April. The sentence was appealed but after a very strenuous campaign by his family to have him reprieved it was made to stand. Cox was hanged on Thursday, 25 April 1929.[62]

■ Track-laying operations.
Source: ESB Archives Photographic Collection.

The scaling down of employment on the scheme was accompanied by a rash of larcenies as men prepared to go home and many determined not to go empty-handed. Much of this petty theft was a result of the relatively low levels of remuneration for those who worked on the Scheme. If the completion of the Shannon Scheme was a major economic and political success for the government, the whole episode was a signal black mark in the state's labour history.

Siemens-Schuckert and the Electrification of the Irish Free State[1]

Gerald O'Beirne & Michael O'Connor

Early in 1924, the Siemens-Schuckertwerke (SSW) directorate in Berlin established contact with the government of the Irish Free State in Dublin, in relation to Shannon Scheme.[2] On 8 February SSW Director H. Wallem presented President Cosgrave and several other ministers with the company's concept, and endorsed the technical and commercial feasibility of the scheme. He outlined the SSW proposals for the generation, transmission and distribution of electricity from the Shannon. At the same time, he stressed that the demands of navigation, fisheries and drainage would be attended to as far as possible. The Free State government decided for its part to call for a detailed report from SSW on the proposals, which was to be presented within six months (by 1 September at the latest). This would be submitted for rigorous appraisal by a team of independent experts to be selected from European countries with hydro-electric generating experience.

The most important points of the meeting in Dublin, notably the fixing of obligations and rights of SSW regarding the preparation of the report, were set out on 26 February 1924 in a letter from G. Campbell, Secretary of the Department of Industry and Commerce, to Wallem at Siemens in Berlin. In a reply the same month, SSW confirmed its acceptance of the contractual terms and conditions. It is noteworthy that the responsible parties in SSW, having decided to undertake this ambitious project, were prepared to agree to unfavourable conditions.[3] However, all the important decisions of the German side have to be viewed in the context of the urgent requirement for high-turnover foreign activities. Germany needed foreign exchange and prestigious foreign projects to help it recover from the First World War and to pay its war reparations.

■ At the construction of the Shannon Scheme at Ardnacrusha. Seated in the front row are Patrick McGilligan (second from the left); T.A. McLaughlin (fourth from left); W.T. Cosgrave, President of the Executive Council of the Irish Free State (fifth from the left); John J. Murphy, first Chairman of the ESB (sixth from left). Various personnel from Siemens are also in the group.

The two letters were published in Dublin in March 1924 as a governmental White Paper, and on 7 March were laid before the Dáil and Seanad.[4]

The most important stipulations in the White Paper were:
1. The Report shall contain binding costs.
2. The Report shall not merely examine the existing market conditions for electricity in the Free State, but shall also analyze the possibilities for future industrial and non-industrial development of the country through the use of cheap electrical energy.
3. The 'Shannon scheme' shall stand up to comparison with other existing proposals for the energy supply of the Free State.

4. Siemens-Bauunion (SBU) shall be engaged for the civil engineering of the project.
5. If the SSW plans (including the modifications which may become necessary) are not approved in their technical and commercial aspects following examination by the government-appointed experts, SSW shall have no recourse to reimbursement for their outlay.
6. The 'Shannon scheme', following its approval, shall be executed either by the government as a state undertaking, or by a private company (with SSW being given first option).
7. In the case of execution as a state undertaking, SSW shall be awarded the contract for all materials and civil works at world market prices.
8. The contract for all civil and hydraulic work shall be offered to the aforementioned SBU at lowest prices (the civil contractor shall, as far as possible, use Irish labour, Irish sub-contractors and Irish materials).

Maintaining the six-month stipulation for the preparation of the electrical, civil, hydraulic and mechanical aspects of the project represented a considerable challenge to the participating firms, and a considerable financial risk. The scope of the project included: the electrical aspects (including generators, switchgear and overhead-line network spanning the Irish Free State), the civil and hydraulic construction (including weirs, water intake works, headrace and tailrace canals, power station foundations with the necessary discharge facilities and the power station superstructure), and the mechanical plant (handled by the turbine construction firm of J.M. Voith of Heidenham, Escher Wyss and Co. of Ravensburg and other German companies). The significance of the scheme for Siemens is evident from the fact that it was the largest foreign contract awarded to a German undertaking since the construction of the Baghdad railway at the end of the nineteenth century.[5]

For SBU it was, in its scope and complexity, by far the largest project yet undertaken up to then. Within the tendering period of six months, specialists from the participating firms undertook extensive investigations in Ireland supported by the Irish government. Siemens' engineers carried out exhaustive geological, hydraulic and other studies on the prospective site. Additionally, extensive contemporary and historical data on current flow and related parametric conditions on the river Shannon was made available. Current and historical river data was of significant value to Siemens in determining water-flow rates along the river Shannon.[6]

On 1 October 1924, one month after the scheduled date, SSW handed detailed project documentation to the Irish Free State government.[7] The SSW project proposal comprised 358 pages and included detailed technical chapters and cost projections. It also contained an important chapter on the effects the scheme would be likely to have on the economic and social development of the Irish Free State.[8]

■ President Cosgrave with his family and Patrick McGilligan (second from right) at the official opening of Ardnacrusha power station, 29 July 1929.
Source: History of the ESB, Manning and McDowell.

The exact costing for the partial and full development was £4.867m and £6.721m respectively. These were all only estimated values. Although the rates for labour and materials were fixed (apart from the usual escalation clauses), the quantities required for the final completion of the project could not, because of their nature, be precisely determined in advance. The proposal also considered the advantages derived from low-cost electrical energy for Irish economic development;[9]

Reporting on the Shannon Scheme following commissioning.
Source: Daily Sketch, 30 May 1930.

these included independence from outside power and fuel suppliers and reduced operating costs, which would significantly improve the nation's productivity. Moreover, relatively low-cost electrical energy could provide a basis for the establishment of many new businesses and industries.

It was anticipated that the Irish Free State would experience the same improvements to agriculture as a consequence of electrification as in Germany.[10] The electric lighting of farmhouses and barns, and the provision of electric drives for agricultural pumps and static machinery, would significantly enhance productivity. Electric motors were excellent for the purposes envisaged because of their simplicity, ease of operation, robustness and universal application.[11]

The SSW report expressed surprise that Ireland's energy requirements had up to then been dependent on imported coal, in spite of the hydro-power potential of the country.[12]

In many respects, it provided a spur for the development of a more independent energy policy by the state, enabling it to pursue one which suited its natural resource base and its political aspirations, while simultaneously contributing to economic diversification. It could be said with some conviction that the kind of decisions taken in the early 1920s set the scene for industrial development subsequently.

The SSW project proposal was submitted in October 1924 by the Irish Free State government to a commission comprising four international experts. The experts, who undertook detailed investigations on location in Ireland, summarized their findings and presented their alternative proposals in a report. The report was handed to the government at the beginning of 1925 (parts of this report were made available earlier). Official publication was in March 1925.[13] The experts had made requests for the project draft to be altered. SSW largely accepted these requests, and subsequently largely implemented them.[14]

In their report, the experts agreed in principle with the conception of Thomas McLaughlin (see Chapter 1) and the Siemens companies, with the following alterations:

1. The scheme should encompass three developmental phases ('(first) partial development', 'further development' and 'final development') instead of the two ('partial development' and 'full development') originally suggested.
2. Navigation from the start should be through the canal, thus eliminating the necessity for a lock through the weir onto the River Shannon.
3. The ship lift (or alternatively a lock) at the power station should be dimensioned for 150-ton ships.
4. The experts suggested that, following construction, the ship lift (or lock) also be used as a fish ladder, as had been done satisfactorily for years in various Swiss power plants.
5. The hydraulic calculation was modified in a few points.
6. The original Siemens proposal for the 'partial development' (altered to 'first partial development') had been for two turbines of each 30,000hp, and, on hydro-economic grounds, a smaller turbine rated at 15,000hp. The experts, however, were of the view that the third turbine should also have a rating of 30,000hp, and that by appropriate design, a high level of efficiency would be obtained with low impaction. They suggested, at first, that a special Kaplan turbine be designed to accommodate the large head of water involved. Alternatively, a double-runner turbine could be used, of which one runner would not be impacted at low loads. The two other turbines should always be operated in the range of maximum efficiency, with the third turbine taking over the rest of the operational load. In the case of a very small total load, only the 'special turbine' should be operated. In this respect, the experts drew attention to a Swedish hydro-electric power station then under construction. Here such a 'special turbine' was being installed, viz. a Kaplan turbine, albeit with the lower head of some 6.50m (this plant was the Lilla Edet power station). As the experts were naturally aware of the difficulties involved in the construction and operation of a Kaplan turbine using a head of 30m and more, they subsequently reserved

their suggestions, but stressed that limiting the third machine to a rating of 15,000hp should to be avoided. Their final judgment was that the question of a double-regulated Kaplan turbine operating with a large head was something to be looked at again only in conjunction with the later installation of further turbo-generator sets.[15]

■ Installation of turbine.
Source: ESB Archives Photographic Collection.

The experts' suggestions increased the cost projections. Instead of the sums £4.867m or 6.180m euro (partial development) and £6.721m 7.962m euro (full development), the new totals calculated by the experts were:

First partial development: £5.209m or 6.614m euro
Further development: £7.188m or 9.127m euro
Final development: £7.870m[16] or 9.993m curo

The estimated cost summary of the Siemens companies (SSW & SBU) and the experts for the Shannon Scheme partial development are outlined in Table 1.[17]

Table 1

		SSW/SBU £	Experts £
A.	Power Station (without transmission network)		
1.	Civil Engineering Part		
	a) storage basin, dams, weir, intake building,		
	headrace, power station, tailrace etc.	2,400,000	2,538,000
	b) Land purchase	35,000	35,000
		2,435,000	2,573,000
2.	Mechanical Part		
	(turbines, cranes, sluice gates, pumps etc.)	131,000	184,530
3.	Electrical Part		
	(generators, power station transformers and		
	switchgear etc.)	174,000	215,700
		2,740,000	2,973,230
B.	100(110) kV overhead lines	284,000	298,535
C.	100(110) kV transformer stations	88,000	75,300
D.	35(38) kV overhead lines	751,000	808,580
E.	35(38) kV transformer stations	156,000	160,500
F.	10 kV overhead lines	178,000	178,000
G.	10 kV transformer stations	35,000	35,000
		4,232,000	4,529,145
	Additionally: ca. 15% for interest during construction period (in the case of the Experts, also during the first operating years) on capital	635,000	679,855
		4,867,000	5,209,000

The estimates of the experts showed some reductions and some increases. The most important of these in the realm of civil engineering were reductions in the dimensions of the headrace canal, making the canal cross-section smaller and thereby lowering construction costs. The bed of the tailrace canal was to be only 22m wide and not 31m. The sum for civil engineering was increased by about 8.5 per cent to cover possible wage increases (approximately £195,000). In mechanical engineering, cost reductions were minimal; increases were anticipated in modifying the weir of the intake building, to accommodate changes in civil engineering, while one turbine rating was increased and piping dimensions changed. In electrical engineering (including the transmission network) reductions were anticipated by the use of outdoor stations in Dublin and Cork, while increases were envisaged as a result of utilizing a 30,000kVA instead of the 15,000kVA generator, and an additional 30,000kVA transformer (10,500/110,000V), an improved switching station, stronger and more reliable construction of the masts for the 100 (110)kV and 35 (38)kV overhead lines, insulator suspension chain extended by one member (seven instead of six, and three instead of two). Thus the estimate of the experts (Siemens estimates in parentheses) gave the following approximate Reichsmark[18] (hereafter RM) and percentage allocations of the total of some £4.529m (£4.232 million) to the individual project items.[19]

Table 2

Civil Engineering Part – 52 (49) million RM	57%	(58%)
Mechanical and Electrical Part (without remote transmission network) – 8 (6) million RM	9%	(7%)
Remote Transmission Network (including transformer stations) – 31 (30) million RM	34%	(35%)
Total – 91 (85) million RM	100%	(100%)
Total electrical part (including remote transmission network) – 35 (33) million RM	39%	(39%)

■ Carl Friedrich von Siemens (1872-1941).

In the summer of 1925 contract negotiations took place between the Department of Industry and Commerce and SSW. The unit prices for all works were established in accordance with then foreseeable circumstances (in the subsequent years, considerable adjustments ensued). The basis for decision on the scope of the work was the projected calculations of Siemens and the experts' report. The prices agreed were based on the binding rates within these projected calculations.

Before the Irish Free State government could award the contract for the Shannon Scheme, and before the first German freighter with plant components reached the docks of Limerick in September 1925,[20] consent had first to be sought from the Dáil for the modified plans, the acquisition of land and the necessary finance for the scheme. The first contract for the 'partial development' of the Shannon Scheme was signed by the Irish government, represented by McGilligan, and by Wallem (for C. Köttgen and R. Werner) representing SSW, on 13 August 1925. The contract completion time was fixed at three and a half years.[21] Before the signing, a meeting of the relevant directors of SSW and SBU had been held on 3 August 1925 under the chairmanship of Carl Friedrich von Siemens, Chairman of the Supervisory Board of Siemens & Halske (S&H) and SSW. Although the firm was extremely eager to accept the contract, it also made extensive and careful preparations for its execution.[22] H. Kress, a Director of SBU, remarked a few months later: 'The assembly was at the time permeated with the conviction that Ireland had embraced almost unimaginable risks with this project. Apart from its obvious complications, only the best personnel and the most reliable machines should be called upon.' Von Siemens himself tersely remarked: 'There shall be no experiments.'[23] This indicates how clearly the participating firms were aware of the risks of the Shannon contract at the time of its signing.

While the contract of August 1925 only covered civil engineering (which was to be sub-contracted by SSW to SBU), the awarding of the electrical and

■ View of power station.
Source: Paddy McGilligan's private collection. Donated to ESB Archive.

mechanical engineering work to SSW in accordance with the White Paper was as good as secured (apart from the possibility of some negotiation on price adjustments, necessitated by the requirement to conform to lower world market prices). This was again confirmed in writing to SSW on the signing of the contract for the civil engineering (with reference to the undertaking of McGilligan in the Dáil in April 1925, giving effect to the terms of the White Paper).[24] This partial contract was not awarded in 1925, as McGilligan needed time to inform himself in depth, and to engage suitable personnel as government consultants.

The contract for electrical and mechanical engineering was signed on 23 June 1926, i.e. some ten months after the contract for the civil engineering (also signed by McGilligan and Wallem). The completion dates of this contract, synchronized with the civil engineering work, were stipulated in the eight various sections at from 30 to 18 months from the date of the relevant order.[25] The preparation of these contracts and the contract negotiations imposed demands on the Irish government never experienced previously, because of the central significance of complicated technical issues and the sheer scale of the project. McGilligan had concerned himself since 1924 in the study of such contracts for the construction of large hydropower plants and extensive transmission networks.[26] Likewise, he had familiarized himself with the legislation, financing, organization, administration, control and application possibilities associated with expertise and experience from abroad. More than technical and scientific expertise was required for the realization of the Shannon Scheme, and this was provided largely by the Siemens companies, by the other German undertakings, and by the many foreign experts.

The Shannon hydro-electric scheme was finally operational when buildings and plant became available for 'commercial use' on 17 October 1929.[27] The building work was not fully completed, but a stage had been reached that met the requirements in the 'Agreement for submission to Arbitration' of 28 February 1929, and where one of the main aims of the government had been achieved, i.e. the delivery of electric current. Many difficulties resulting in delays had to be overcome, including labour disputes from the start of work in 1925 until January 1926, inclement weather and waterlogged ground, and problems on the headrace canal.[28] Other unforeseen problems were subsequent changes to specifications and the scope of work already underway, administrative obstacles, land acquisition, low productivity because of the inexperience of the labour force, shortage of Irish specialist workers, accidents (especially fires), and most of all, the sinking of the cargo steamer SS *Arabia* underway from Emden to Limerick in March 1926, holding up vital supplies for work on the headrace including four locomotives and 50 km of railway track.

The Free State government decided that there should be no application of the penalty clause as a result of all these unforeseen delays, on the recommendation of Professor Rishworth, the Chief Engineer of civil engineering, in a memorandum of 17 October 1929. In this he fully recognized the justification of the contracted party's request for an extension to the construction period. Rishworth, whose uncompromising stance in the years before, and afterwards, in relation to the large financial losses was a major source of acrimony with the Siemens companies, nevertheless presented in the memorandum a glowing picture of achievement on the part the German contractors. He also expressed the view that it was doubtful if any other firm would have undertaken the Shannon Scheme on such unfavourable conditions. Rishworth wrote:

> An arbitration board would … recognise the response of Dr von Siemens in May 1928 to the Minister's demand for expediting work when additional plant in the form of 32 locomotives, 200 wagons, rail track, steam shovels and rock-crushing equipment were utilised, a step that led to the plant being brought into commercial operation at least four months earlier than would otherwise have been the case … and I believe that no other contractor would have made such a gesture at that stage of construction, taking into consideration the financial losses to date, and the possibility of being relieved of any penalties by an arbitrator … Furthermore, I consider the progress during the past year to fifteen months a magnificent effort on the part of the contractors to overcome the delays in the earlier stages of work. The period of three years was extremely short for the amount of work involved and could only have been achieved by the extravagant use of plant and superb organisation.[29]

The official opening of the Shannon Scheme was carried out by President Cosgrave on 22 July 1929. Following the blessing by The Most Rev. Dr Fogarty, Bishop of Killaloe, Cosgrave threw the switch that opened the sluice gates for the waters of the Shannon to flow into the headrace canal. The assembly of guests consisted of representatives of the Irish government, both houses of the Oireachtas, the universities, the army, the engineering institutions, the World Power Conference, the Electricity Supply Board (ESB), various foreign representatives, the Siemens companies, other undertakings and organizations, and many private and civic dignitaries. In total almost 1000 people watched the opening of a new chapter of Irish history. The Dáil representation included de Valera with members from his Fianna Fáil party. ESB representatives included Murray, McLaughlin and Foley. The Siemens participation included Baron von Graevenitz (nephew of von Siemens, who was active as advisor on the Shannon

■ Opening day in Turbine Hall.
Source: ESB Archives Photographic Collection.

Scheme for SSW in Ireland from 1929) and Uitting from Berlin (who had played a key role in the project). The opening was also attended by von Dehn,[30] the German consul in Dublin. Cosgrave, in his opening speech, stressed the enormous value of the Shannon Scheme for the future development of the state. He also pointed out that questions previously raised frequently with strong pessimistic undertones, namely the estimated construction costs and the demand for such quantities of electrical energy, had now been clearly answered. In the first place, the extra costs to the Free State up to then were less than 5 per cent of the estimated cost; secondly, the growth rate in recent years more than justified the most optimistic predictions.[31] The importance of the project in the creation and furtherance, both abroad and in Ireland itself, of trust in the new Irish state and its enterprise was stressed by Cosgrave: 'In this convincingly manifest form, it has been demonstrated that the Irish Free State is in a position to execute, quickly, efficiently and economically, a hydro-electric project equal to any other in Europe. Thus, here and elsewhere, a firm foundation of confidence has been established in our ability to bring about that economic development of great national embrace which we all desire.'

The commercial supply of electric current from the Shannon power station, initially over a duplex 110kV line to Inchicore and to Ring IV, commenced on 24 October 1929.[32] An important component of the Shannon Scheme was the high and medium voltage network, which provided a comprehensive supply throughout the state. This overhead line network, with a total length of about 3,400 km, down to the 10kV level, was erected by SSW in the period from 1926 to 1929. This part of the contract from the government represented the largest-ever overhead line contract awarded to a single firm up to then, and for many decades subsequently.[33]

The extraordinarily large scale of the Shannon Scheme, even in the 'partial development' phase, necessitated the mobilization of enormous financial resources. Large sums of money would have to be expended before part payment would be received from the Irish Free State government for work undertaken. This financial burden was particularly onerous for the main contractor, SSW. In total, a sum of some 90 million RM was required at the start for the contract to finance the civil, mechanical and electrical engineering. Moreover, financing was required not just for the Shannon Scheme, but also for other contingencies within S & H and SSW. It was, therefore, necessary that the existing financial structure be expanded.[34] Table 3 shows the totals of the agreed quantities and price index for the civil engineering involved in the 'partial development' of the Scheme, which was integrated into the contract of 13 August 1925.[35] The quantities were estimated and not binding, whereas the unit prices were binding. Therefore, the totals given in Table 3 were only estimates based on the circumstances foreseen at the time. Table 3 also shows the figures calculated by SSW in the 'Final Account' for work carried out by SBU and the amounts recognized by the Chief Engineer for the Final Certificate of operation.[36]

Table 3 (NOTE: STG£1 = 20 SHILLINGS)

		Contract Sum August 1925 (shillings)	Final A/C August 1930 (shillings)	Final Cert. October 1930 (shillings)
Ia.	Storage basin between Banagher and Killaloe	4,247,024.90	2,043,636.57	1,079,213.63
Ib.	Dams on both banks of the Shannon about the water storage	4,487,440.20	2,861,006.32	2,054,472.43
II	Weir and intake building	4,158,107.70	4,677,955.52	4,337,228.74
III	Headrace canal	14,006,859.00	22,800,581.78	21,950,488.36
IV	Road bridges over the headrace canal	752,450.40	1,465,478.80	1,453,909.96
V	Power station	5,787,434.00	10,699,534.84	9,941,420.71
VI	Tailrace canal	5,946,770.00	10,688,185.61	7,837,778.71
VII	Shannon reinforcement (between Corbaliy and Limerick)	5,975,860.00	83,389.68	————
VIII	Railway connection Longpavement to power station	287,868.00	33,492.79	332,646.99
IX	Site power station	————	————	————
X	General	————	————	————
	The costs for IX and X are distributed in the work in other sections.			
XI	Base sills on Shannon	395,906.00	omitted	omitted
		46,045,720.20	55,653,261.91	48,987,159.53
	Work on securing of dams to Point 0.12 of Specification Part I (maximum permissible 600,000 shillings)	600,000.00	600,000.00	600,000.00
		46,645,720.20	56,253,261.91	49,587,159.53
	Later in addition:			
	Roads	————	394,325.51	392,075.12
	Double lock	————	3,168,308.39	2,260,049.95
		46,645,720.20	59,815,895.81	52,239,284.60

Table 3 shows that the estimated contracted amounts were considerably exceeded, and that SBU were refused a claim amounting to almost 7.6 million shillings by the Chief Engineer.

Regarding the contracted amounts, it has to be said that these had increased to over 50 million shillings by completion of the plant, due especially to additional new works (e.g. the double sluices), although some items had to be reduced in scope or fully omitted (Ia, VII, XI); Ib was reduced because the weir was finally located farther upriver than originally planned, and the headrace canal, Item III, therefore became longer and more expensive. However, several further millions had to be added to the already mentioned shortfall of 7.6 million shillings. SBU had calculated in the 'Final Account' also the following items for the period up to 28 June 1930 (for simplicity and transparency, they are summarized in Table 4, with the amounts allowed by the 'Engineer' also shown):

Table 4

	Final Account August 1930 (shillings)	Final Certificate October 1930 (shillings)
Component of wage increase over basic wage to be met by contractual party, in accordance with Point 7 of the 'Articles of Agreement'	4,610,781.84	4,300,295.76
Miscellaneous items e.g. tax refunds, minor works etc.	434,266.75	118,095.82
Further extra costs, responsibility for which was laid with the 'Engineer' and the Irish contractual party (for details, see below)	11,852,812.00	25,000.00
	16,897,860.59	4,443,391.58
Plus the partial amount already calculated above	59,815,895.81	52,239,284.60
Total amounts of 'Final Account' and 'Final Certificate'	76,713,756.40	56,682,676.18

The last item, 'Further extra costs', includes additional costs, for some of which explanations have already been given earlier. In the 'Final Account', explanations for the additional costs are detailed along the following lines (only the largest and most revealing items are mentioned below):

1. Rejection by the 'Engineer' of the obligation to award wage rises to suitable unskilled labour, which were absolutely necessary, and also within the terms of the contract (c. 4.5 million shillings).
2. Payment of exceptionally high premiums for the insurance of unsuitable workers whom SBU had been compelled to employ (c. 1.1 million shillings).
3. Recruitment of additional skilled labour from Germany, as the 'Engineer' had not been prepared to approve the wage increases necessary for qualified workers (c. 350,000 shillings).
4. Refusal of the 'Engineer', prior to the completion of the work, to reach binding decisions regarding justified extensions to the deadlines for construction work (c. 4.5 million shillings).
5. Interruption of work and delays caused by late actions and instructions on the part of the Irish contractual partner (c. 1.0 million shillings).

The attitude of the Chief Engineer was the subject of repeated complaints by the German contractors. It was considered that he did not act as a neutral and independent mediator between the contractual parties. Moreover, it was the view of the German companies that he was subservient to the wishes of the Minister for Industry and Commerce, who appeared at the time to take this for granted. Furthermore, the Chief Engineer turned to the Minister regarding decisions on important matters that he should have decided on himself.[37] The German companies complied with repeated Irish requests to accelerate construction, even though an entitlement to 'extension of deadlines' was firmly rooted in the conditions of the contract. Von Siemens had made generous concessions to the Minister for Industry and Commerce in 1928, and, in particular, had ensured that additional construction machinery and more locomotives were sent to Ireland. This resulted in major disruption to the planned execution and costing of the entire project, as extra materials, machines and manpower had to be deployed rapidly, resulting in severe congestion in workshops and living quarters, and major overruns in the cost projections. It was clear to the Siemens companies from the start that a considerable part of the disputed amounts would in all probability not be conceded. Moreover, earlier concessions had most likely weakened their claim. Nevertheless, it was seen as 'useful' to press these demands in order to create a stronger basis for negotiation. The total outlay by SSW as of 31 December 1929 and according to the accounted figures (excluding work in hand) was 80,063,320 shillings, to which was added, for the period from 1 January 1930 to the end of construction, some 2,173,000 shillings (estimated in May 1930). These amounts rendered a total of cost at the end of construction of approximately 82,236,320 shillings.[38] SBU losses have been summarized in Table 5.

Table 5

		(shillings)
(a)	Total SBU costs up to end of construction (partially estimated)	82,236,320.00
(b)	Siemens claim in 'Final Account' of 16 August 1930	76,713,756.40
(c)	Residual amount claimed in Siemens 'Final Account' (because up to the 28th June 1930 for the calculations in the 'Final Account', only an amount of 55,595,203.18 shillings had been received)	21,118,553.22
(d)	Amount recognised by the 'Engineer' in the 'Final Certificate' dated 21st October 1930	56,682,676.18
(e)	Amount already paid by Irish contractual party for work up to 28th June 1930 according to the 'Final Certificate' (55,948,138.00 shillings for 'Certificates' 1 to 52, plus 94,150.75 shillings refund of duty and tax)	56,042,288.75
(f)	Remaining to be paid to Siemens as of 21st October 1930 (the 150 000 shillings mentioned in the 'Final Certificate' as 'retention monies' in accordance with Section 0.54 of the Specifications Part I of contract dated 13th August 1930 have not been deducted here) [(d) — (e)]	640,387.43
(g)	Preliminary loss by SBU on the Partial Development of the Shannon Scheme on the basis of the figure in the 'Final Certificate' [(a) - (d)] or alternatively (a) — (e) — (f)]	25,553,643.82 25.6 million

■ Construction work at intake building.
Source: Siemens Archive.

The fact that the Siemens companies emerged from the 'partial development' phase of the Shannon Scheme with an indicated loss of some 25.6 million RM is hardly surprising.[39] Many factors contributed to this. Firstly, the prices agreed by SBU following the contract negotiations were too low. SSW in the summer of 1924 had combined their costs for electrical and mechanical engineering with those of SBU for civil works and prepared a profitability calculation, as required by the White Paper. In this 'pre-contract', SSW was obliged to erect a power station and national grid that would not only be technically satisfactory, but would also return an acceptable operating profit within a few years.

SBU, whose costs represented the greatest part of the total amount, was therefore requested by SSW to re-check its pricing and costings. SBU did this, and submitted to SSW a new cost schedule with prices considerably lower than previously,[40] to ensure the acceptance of the financial aspects of the scheme by the Irish government. Consequently, they were used by the Siemens companies as the basis for the contract of 13 August 1925 for civil engineering work. It is possible that these prices were even further reduced in the course of the contract negotiations with Professor Rishworth, the Chief Engineer.[41] From existing data, it is not possible to determine with certainty what factors led SBU to its decision about price reductions.[42] In the report of May 1930, a 'pre-calculated performance value' approaching some 59.8 million shillings in the 'Final Account' produced a pre-calculated profit of almost 615,000 shillings, an extremely modest amount considering the scale of the contract. The context which made this acceptable was that German industry was in difficulties and badly needed to win international contracts to earn foreign currency, which entailed high-risk business on unfavourable terms.[43] This was clearly a factor in taking on the Shannon contract. It is not surprising that, with the difficult economic circumstances of the time and the unfavourable industrial conditions in Ireland, the decision-reaching process within the Siemens companies was, to say the least, fraught. With the difference between success and failure balanced on a knife-edge, the opinions of key personnel would have been divided. Nonetheless, these were harsh times and the prevailing view must have been: nothing ventured, nothing gained.

There were a number of reasons why the original estimates were so wide of the mark and why the scale of additional work-in-hand grew disproportionately along with the programme delays. These included the huge problem in recruiting suitable manpower, inclement weather, unfavourable ground conditions and complicated geological formations, transport difficulties between harbour and site, and delays by the client and its representatives. To a large extent, the increase of the Scheme in losses and the deterioration of relationships between Siemens and the Irish client were, in the opinion of the former, attributable to the 'inappropriate' conduct of the Chief Engineer. The more serious of the problems, which had arisen from the first major differences of opinion, were repeatedly referred to in correspondence and in personal meetings between McGilligan and von Siemens.[44]

McGilligan again and again drew attention to the high reputation of the Siemens concern and to how the company's good name might be at stake. Correspondingly, von Siemens replied in a letter of 2 November 1927 that he was more than aware that the name of Siemens was tied to the success of the

Shannon Scheme, and that it represented for the German side much more than a mere business venture. What was at stake was nothing less than the national interest (of Germany). He wrote that it was of paramount importance, for both the reputation of his firm and the standing of the Irish government, that nothing should stand in the way of the earliest possible supply of electric current from the Shannon. In a letter of 1 September 1930 to the Minister in connection with the 'Final Account', von Siemens expressed his regret over the troubled relationship with the Chief Engineer. He pointed out that he considered some additional demands as fair and justified, and must insist on these being met.[45] In his reply letter of 15 September 1930, the Minister shared von Siemens' regret, but made clear that it was his duty to protect the Irish Free State from financial burdens for which it was not responsible.[46] As early as 1928, he had stressed to von Siemens that he was answerable to the Dáil and had to give due account for all expenditures. For this reason, there was no way he could agree to 'unjustified' payments being made to the contracted partner.[47]

In the view of SBU, as the above calculations indicate, there still existed legitimate extra claims in the order of several million shillings. The main contractor, SSW, continued to press for these.[48] At the same time there were discussions within the Siemens firms on whether partial concessions should be made in the interests of good relations.

A position tending towards conciliation appears to have been adopted by, among others, von Siemens as well as by Baron von Graevenitz and the Dublin solicitor, Cox. The views of the latter two apparently had a strong influence on the head of the firm. Von Siemens made it clear to the German Foreign Office, which had become involved as an intermediary, that he 'would extremely regret' if the House of Siemens had to make a damaging appearance in a civil court case 'in the full glare of publicity', as a consequence of which the success of the project and its worldwide reputation could be tarnished. He wrote that he would value an amicable settlement that would include 'compensation' in the form of further business from the Irish government, not necessarily in the energy sector, but, for example, in the area of telephone systems. At the end of 1931, when the matter had still not come to a conclusion, von Siemens declared that 'he wished for a swift settlement' with the Irish government on two grounds: firstly, in order not to jeopardize further business, and secondly, having due regard to the balance sheets of the Siemens companies.[49]

■ Erection of the main gates with the finished submerged curtain wall behind them.
Source: Siemens, Progress on the Shannon, Number 14, November 1929. Front Page.

Meanwhile, the financial disagreements between the parties had entered the public domain. In the face of rumours circulating in a number of newspapers of the huge losses for Siemens and of an impending legal action by the Siemens company against the Irish Free State, the Siemens management felt compelled to issue a placatory press release on 21 January 1931. In this, it was pointed out that disputes were by no means unusual in such large and complicated projects. Finally, a stage was reached where both parties felt that an understanding could be reached on the outstanding financial issues of the Shannon Scheme's 'partial development' phase. At the start of 1932, the Siemens companies were officially advised by the Department of Industry and Commerce that a closing payment of £150,000 had been authorized.[50] The German side declared its satisfaction with this relatively small amount, and discontinued its legal action.

This payment of £150,000 almost certainly contained the sum of some 640,000 shillings still outstanding since the issue of the 'Final Certificate' in 1930.[51] The final losses of SBU have been summarized in Table 6.

Table 6 (NOTE: STG£1 = 20 SHILLINGS)

		(shillings)
(a)	Preliminary loss by SBU as shown above	ca. 25.6 million
(b)	Amount of 640,000 shillings recognised in the 'Final Certificate' but apparently not paid by 1932	ca. 0.6 million
(c)	Residual payment of £150,000 = 3 million shillings agreed by Irish government in 1932	3.0 million
(d)	Final loss by SBU on the Partial Development of the Shannon Scheme [(a) + (b) - (c)]	ca. 23.2 million

Converted to RM and taking into account the effect of the sterling devaluation of 1931 on the final government payment, the final total loss suffered was approximately 24.2 million RM. The SBU losses were taken over by S & H and SSW.[52] As SSW with its own resources had been involved in the electrical aspects of the Shannon Scheme, and had made a profit for the electrical and mechanical work,[53] the net total losses absorbed by the Siemens companies was reduced to 21.7 million RM. The closing accounts of SBU reflect the development of the 'concern debt' to its creditors S & H and SSW for the Ireland account. The accounts showed in particular that the accumulated debt, over the years to 30 June 1930, of 10 million RM for S & H and some 18.5 million RM for SSW was suddenly on 30 September 1930 reduced to 5.5 million RM for each. The complete elimination of the debt is then indicated by the closing accounts for the third quarter of 1932. The sums of somewhat more than 5.2 million RM each for S & H and SSW still showing on 30 June were reduced to zero as of 30 September.[54] The final transactions for the sharing and booking of the Shannon Scheme losses were specifically referred to in the business reports and balance sheets of S & H and SSW for the year 1931/32. To cover the residual loss of 4.5 million RM each, both firms drew on special reserves 'provided for such exceptional cases' (accumulated at 14.0 million RM from the business year 1925/26 to 1929/30 in the case of SSW, and at 12.5 million RM from 1926/27 to 1929/30 in the case of S & H.

These losses were especially unwelcome at that time, since even without them, the business returns for all the Siemens companies had significantly deteriorated since 1928/29 because of the world economic depression. S & H in 1931/32, the year of accounting for the residual Shannon Scheme losses, would achieve a net profit of scarcely 7.0 million RM (compared with 16 million RM for 1928/29), while SSW reported no profit for that year, nor indeed for 1930/31 or 1932/33 (as against a profit of 15.5 million RM in 1928/29).[55]

The relatively unfavourable position of the contractors was, of course, to the advantage of the Free State government and the Department of Industry and Commerce. The Irish side, as was its right, endeavoured to interpret the conditions of contract as far as it could to its own advantage. The attitude of the Minister to the additional claims on the part of German companies was by now quite clear. In the Dáil the Minister had to dispel fears of drastic cost escalation. In doing this, he contrived to strengthen the position of the government vis-à-vis the contracting parties. At the end of 1931 Professor Meyer-Peter of Zurich was appointed to act as arbitrator.[56] He advised a further and final payment of between £120,000 and £170,000 to the Siemens companies as fair. From this, the sum of £150,000 was decided on. Minister McGilligan considered this amount to be just about defendable and in keeping with the promise implied in a speech during the original debates on the Shannon scheme in the Dáil. He had implied then that the amount to be paid by the Irish Free State to the contractors would not exceed more than 10 per cent of the initial contract amount.[57]

In accordance with the Shannon Electricity Act, 1925, Section 11.5, the Free State government had initially allocated the amount of £5.21m for the financing of the Shannon Scheme's 'first development' phase, viz. for the generation of electrical energy and its transmission to 10kV transformers, excluding local distribution networks. In addition, the Minister for Industry and Commerce in 1929 had to procure additional funds to meet further costs of over £600,000 (not contained in the contracts of 1925 and 1926). These extra monies were for the capitalization of compensation paid to landowners for the erection of pylons on their land and property, for administration and supervision, and for unforeseen extras within the scope of the contract.

■ View of power station.
Source: ESB Archives Photographic Collection.

An amount of £625,000 was approved by the Electricity (Finance) Act, 1929, so that a total of £5.835m was then available, although this included £132,450 for the improvement of navigation.[58] According to ESB data, the capital costs for the Shannon Scheme plant handed over by the Minister for Industry and Commerce to the Board up to 31 March 1931 were some £5.58m.[59] Added to the £5.835m from the Acts up to 1929, there followed £335,000 as the amount for the Shannon Scheme's 'final development'. Included in this was the £150,000 for satisfying Siemens' claims. This amount was approved under the Electricity (Supply) (Amendment) Act, 1932, by the new Fianna Fáil government. Thus, the total amount advanced by the Minister for Finance for the first partial development was £6.17m.[60] The increase in 1929 to £5.835m attracted some criticism in parliament because the additional amount contained items that had not been mentioned by the Minister for Industry and Commerce in 1925. The settlement of 1932 with SSW (the payment of the £150,000) would have had a marginal effect on the financial consequence of the Scheme's first partial development for the government. The Siemens companies, on the other hand, had to absorb painful losses during a global recession. In all, the Free State government had by 1932 provided £10.7m for the first stages of the national electrification programme, i.e. the Shannon Scheme's 'partial development', and for the financial requirements of the ESB.[61]

The success of the start-up stage of the national electrification of the Irish Free State has never been seriously disputed. The electrification project, described by de Valera as an 'experiment of great sociological value,'[62] attracted wide praise in the

Dáil as 'an outstanding and flagrant success and to the credit of this country'.[63] In the Seanad Barrington declared that the Free State had in a record time acquired an electricity supply system of which any nation could be proud.[64] At the end of 1940 MacEntee in retrospect expressed the view that 'the development of our water power does put us in a position of independence and does give us a national task which has important reactions upon our psychology. I think it is true to say that the fact that we were able, so soon after the unfortunate civil war, to undertake the development of the Shannon Scheme had a good effect upon us all. We can all look back and take equal pride in the fact that there were some people who had the courage and the vision to tackle the project at that time.'[65]

The success of the Shannon Scheme earned for the participating German firms a worldwide reputation, which subsequently had a favourable effect on many aspects of their business and turnover, serving as a good reference plant to impress prospective customers who wished to pursue similar projects. Although Siemens' activity in Ireland in the 1920s and 1930s was almost exclusively confined to the field of electricity generation and distribution, in later years, again gaining by the goodwill resulting from the Shannon Scheme, its business expanded into other areas. While in the short term for Siemens the Shannon Scheme generated significant losses, from a more long-term perspective it could be viewed as a loss leader. For the House of Siemens, the execution of the Shannon Scheme was the one single event that marked the reappearance of the firm on the world electrical scene following the gloom of the Great War and its aftermath. It remains as one of the major landmarks in the history of the company.[66]

The Railway System
for the Shannon Scheme

Brendan Delany

The works specified in the contract for the Shannon Scheme, which was signed on 13 August 1925 between the Free State and Siemens, were completed within about four years. This would not have been possible without the railway system that was installed at Ardnacrusha for the construction phase of the project.

Siemens-Schuckertwerke sub-contracted the civil engineering work for the scheme to its sister company, Siemens-Bauunion. This company took responsibility for creating the railway system required to support all the construction work. Even by today's standards, the scale of the work involved was huge, and the railway system linked the entire site. It had to accommodate 130 steam locomotives and eight electric locomotives; estimates of the number of railway wagons used vary between 1800 and 3000, not counting specialized equipment that operated on tracks.[1]

After the formal signing of the contract Siemens arranged for the immediate despatch of some key personnel to Ireland. These early groups arrived by ship to both Queenstown (Cobh)[2] and Kingstown (Dún Laoghaire) and travelled on mainline trains to Limerick. One of the first tasks to be undertaken by the German and Irish engineers was to complete their initial fieldwork, conducting surveys of Parteen, Ballykeelaun, Clonlara, O'Briensbridge and Killaloe. This information was of critical importance in assessing what needed to be done to prepare site

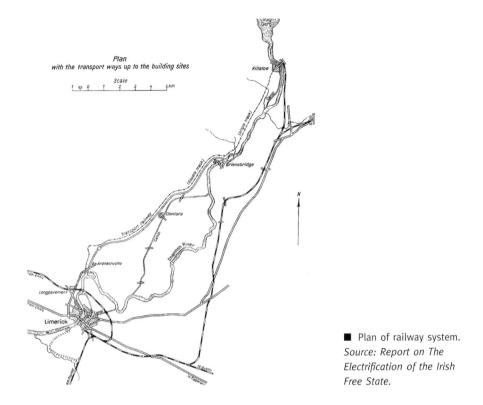

Plan
with the transport ways up to the building sites

■ Plan of railway system.
*Source: Report on The
Electrification of the Irish
Free State.*

offices, accommodation, and the supporting railway network. The journal
Structural Engineer employed the services of a contemporary novelist, Valentine
Williams, to record the progress of the scheme. His account reveals that conditions
for those carrying out these preliminary investigations were far from ideal:

> A Titan's task confronted these peaceful invaders. Ireland could bring
> almost nothing to their aid save the more or less willing arms of her
> unskilled labour. The German engineers found themselves in a virtual
> roadless tract of desolate pastureland with nought save a couple of miserable
> hamlets all along the way from Limerick to Killaloe. There was no power
> station they could utilise, no railway to transport the plant to the building
> sites, no fuel except imported, and at Limerick docks totally inadequate
> facilities for handling the fabulous quantities of materials required … As
> they inhaled the soft and sluggish Shannon air and watched the ragged

■ Unloading of locomotive from steamer for Ardnacrusha.
Source: Siemens, Progress on the Shannon, Number 1, October 1926.

natives pottering about their wretched and dim cabbage patches in the leisurely manner peculiar to the West of Ireland peasantry, hearts less valiant than those of the professional engineer must have quailed before the magnitude of the undertaking.[3]

The first task was to transport specialist equipment from Germany to Ireland. The next step was to bring it from the docks in Limerick and Dublin to Ardnacrusha and the other construction sites. Given the state of the road network, road haulage was not an option and a special railway system had to be constructed as a priority. This was a task for which Siemens-Bauunion had expertise, the construction of the Baghdad Railway line being the most dramatic example.[4] The major challenge was to meet the very tight targets for setting up an integrated, but stand-alone, railway system which would enable the overall project to be completed within the contract deadline.

In their initial proposal document, 'The Electrification of the Irish Free State – The Shannon Scheme', Siemens had already set out their plans to use a custombuilt railway network to facilitate the transport of materials, equipment and heavy plant. In this the company stated its intention to utilize the harbour at Foynes or Cork for the trans-shipment of all the heavy gear, large-sized machines and spare parts originating in Emden and Hamburg; Limerick harbour would be used to import all light gear, building materials, and mechanical plant, provided the planned connecting line between Limerick and the existing line could be completed in time. What happened in reality was that Foynes and Cork were not used; the heaviest materials were shipped to Dublin port, and the rest to the docks in Limerick. The original intention was to construct a full-gauge railway from the site of the power station directly to Limerick harbour via Longpavement. In the event, the railway line was brought only as far as Thomondgate, a stretch of waste ground in Longpavement. Thus the materials and plant were taken from the docks to Longpavement, which was the start of the railway network for onward transportation to their final destination. Among the first shipments to arrive were lorries which were used to transport the equipment and materials from the docks to Longpavement. An electrically operated derrick and two oil cranes were quickly installed at the quayside in Limerick to assist with the unloading process. Siemens' 1924 proposal document stated:

> Before a beginning can be made on the work proper, a means of conveyance is to be provided alongside the future construction sites, in the form of a double-track narrow-gauge railway with 90cm (3ft) gauge. This is to commence at the railway station at Longpavement and to run alongside the public highway for some distance beyond Quinspool Bridge. Thence it is to proceed across country to the site of the future power-house and is to be continued along the right bank of the head race of the planned canal as far as the canal inlet construction at O'Briensbridge. One track is to be extended further to Killaloe to connect the works situated there to Longpavement.
>
> The construction of the narrow-gauge connecting line must be completed as soon as possible, so as to allow the transport of the necessary heavy gear to the construction sites and the construction work proper to commence with the least delay. For this purpose a portion of the track

and some rolling-stock will be sent at once by rail from Foynes to Longpavement, where a beginning is to be made on the construction of the first stretches of the line between the latter place and the powerhouse. The remainder of the track and rolling-stock can, we assume, be transported by water up-river through the ship canal as far as Clonlara. From the latter place the track is to be laid downstream along the Headrace in the direction of the power station and upstream in the direction of O'Briensbridge. In this way it will be possible to lay the proposed stretch of connecting line, with a length of roughly 20km, in a very short time. It is proposed to work the connecting line with steam locomotives. A number of turn-outs are provided to facilitate the handling of the traffic. Sufficient spur-lines leading to the various workings are contemplated. By these means it will be possible to keep up continual internal traffic between the various workings themselves, the importance of which, considering the necessity for the exchange of gear, and building materials, cannot be undervalued.[5]

Siemens-Bauunion chartered three large 2000-ton freight ships to shuttle between Germany and Limerick, along with a range of smaller craft. Within the first few months, 87 steamers had left 30,000 tons of equipment at Limerick docks, including locomotives, small trucks, bucket dredgers, bank-building machines, concrete-mixers, air compressors, barges, tugs, launches and pontoons. After these initial consignments, a steamer came every fortnight or three weeks. Sadly one, the SS *Arabia*, was lost at sea in 1926, with the loss of nineteen crew, when en route from Emden to Limerick, with key items of plant on board.

As the cranes at Limerick harbour could only handle loads up to 20 tons the heavy equipment was directed to Dublin port, where a 100-ton crane was available. A specially designed rail truck with a capacity to handle loads up to 50 tons had to be provided to transport these loads from Dublin to Limerick, and then from Longpavement to Ardnacrusha. Some of the loads, although they weighed less than the 50-ton limit, had to be transported by road because their dimensions exceeded that which could be handled using the railway gauge. The road network from Limerick harbour to Longpavement had also to be considerably improved in a short space of time. It was soon discovered after some initial survey work that spacious cellars existed under the streets in many parts of Limerick and that the road which formed the ceiling of some of these cellars was only one foot thick and therefore most unlikely to withstand the pressure of large vehicles carrying weights up to 35 tons. Careful planning was therefore required to find a special route that avoided such difficulties.[6]

The scale of the project was huge even by today's standards. The inventory of the plant and material used throughout the project is summarized in Table 1.

Table 1

Plant

6 large bucket dredgers on rails, each about 220 tons

3 large bank-building machines on rails, each about 240 tons

27 smaller dredgers and shovel excavators on rails and caterpillars

130 steam locomotives

8 electric locomotives

31 portable air compressors

13 portable concrete mixers

8 tower cranes

3 cableways, each 310m long

1,770 railway wagons

20 road trucks

31 barges, tugs, launches and pontoons

Material

23,000 m³ timber

2,670 tons reinforcing steel for concrete

65,000 tons of cement

10,100 tons fuel oil

110,000 tons coal

700 tons explosives

Source: G. O'Beirne, History of Siemens in Ireland 1925–2000 *(Dublin 2000), p. 50. B.N. Sweeney lists other items of plant, including nine diesel generators, a workshop with over fifty machine tools, a brass foundry, a rope-splicer, a beltshop, an acetylene and oxygen plant, a sawmill, a carpenter's workshop, an explosives store, turbines, transformers, switchgear, transmission masts, insulaters, and an overhead conductors; see 'The Building of Ardnacrusha',* Trans. Instit. Engineers of Ireland, *vol. 119 (1995/96).*

■ Conveying broken stones.
Source: Siemens, Progress on the Shannon, Number 12, September 1927.

In addition to the plant and materials enumerated in Table 1, various sources have confirmed that about 7.5 million cubic metres of earth and 1.25 million cubic metres of rock were excavated. Practically all of this work, and the installation of the physical plant and transport of materials, would have relied on the railway system.

The railway system used a track of waste ground at Thomondgate in Long-pavement as the location for its terminus. McGrath provides an overview:

> The line, double track for part of the way, ran along a road for a short distance and then crossed the standard-gauge Limerick-Ennis line on the level. The crossing was protected by a stop arm on each side, this signal showing "road clear" to the industrial railway except when a standard-gauge train was due. Beyond this crossing the line took to the fields, skirted the tail-race works and continued on through Co. Clare to O'Briens-bridge, eight miles away. An extensive network of branch lines ran to the various huge excavators and dredgers at work throughout the countryside. This railway was to utilise a gauge of 900 millimetres (a little under 2ft and

eleven and a half inches) and ancillary to it was a web of the 600 milli-metres (one foot and eleven and five eighths inches) gauge lines of light pre-fabricated track capable of being moved about as the work progressed.[7]

Approximately 100 km of narrow-gauge railway was used; according to Garbotz, this required '128,000m rails (Preussen 11) weighing 3,580 tons, 241 switches 12m long weighing 550 tons, small fittings of a total weight of about 500 tons, 120,000 timber sleepers … and as an initial trial on a ballasted section 35,000 iron sleepers'.[8] Parts of the railway line had to be moved frequently, and a specially devised track-shifting machine was utilized for that purpose. Duffy highlights the fact that the locomotives were not the only equipment to use the narrow-gauge railway:

■ Machine for moving track of the Arbens-Kammerer type.
Source: Siemens, Progress on the Shannon, Number 5, February 1927.

Six multiple-bucket electrically powered excavators were used during the course of the work. These travelled on rails parallel to the line of the races (Head Race & Tail Race). The buckets scooped up the earth, dropped it into a large hopper where it was fed into wagons and then taken to the Absetzer or Transporter to be used in the building of the embankments. Three Absetzers were used during the construction of the embankments. These machines were developed originally for work in the coalmines in Germany and the Shannon Scheme was the first location where they were used in embankment building. They were capable of dropping material from a height of 15 m, which ensured excellent compaction, over an oper-ating width of 40 m. …

As well as the massive amounts of excavation and fill, an enormous quantity of concreting work had to be carried out during the works. Much of this latter work was carried out using two cable cranes. Each crane consisted of twin steel towers, each 36 m high, connected by a cable spanning the 325 m distance between the towers. The towers incorporated concrete mixers which fed directly into buckets of the cable cranes. These cranes were electrically operated, and as they could move on rails they could cover an area of 35,000 sq. m. One of the machines was used to place some 60,000 cu.m of concrete in eleven months.[9]

According to Mc Grath all the engines were 0-4-0 tanks (see Table 2 for a listing of locomotives used on the scheme). Initially they were fitted with stove-pipe chimneys; some had low squat chimneys. Only minor repairs were carried out on site; for the heavier repairs and overhauls they were returned to Germany. It is probable that some locomotives were acquired by Siemens-Bauunion secondhand, and therefore it would be extremely difficult to ascertain details of manufacture, or when they came to Ireland, whereas those listed in Table 2 can be traced from

Table 2   Locomotives used on the Shannon Scheme

No. of Eng.	Maker	Date	HP	Cylinders	Gauge
3	Krauss	1920	160	320 x 400	900
16	Henschel	1925	160	310 x 430	900
16	Henschel	1925	200	340 x 430	900
18	Borsig	1925	220	340 x 400	900
19	Hanomag	1925	200	330 x 430	900
21	Rheinische	1925	220	350 x 350	900
1	Metalwarren	n/a	n/a	n/a	900
2	Henschel	1919	40	185 x 250	600
10	Linke	1923	50	215 x 300	600
1	A. Jung	1920	40	190 x 300	600

Source: W. Mc Grath, 'Narrow Gauge Railway of the Shannon Scheme', The Narrow Gauge No. 75, Spring (1977).

the manufacturers' records, as they were purchased for dispatch to this project. An idea of using only electric locomotives throughout the scheme, which would have been more economical in terms of staffing and energy consumption, had to be abandoned because of 'the unfavourable terms of delivery for the necessary electric locomotives, transformers, rectifiers, as well as the necessity of changing the dredgers for direct current'.[10]

The labourers who laid the tracks had a particularly difficult and dangerous job. Tracks often had to be laid quickly and then as soon as construction on one particular section of the site was completed, rapidly dismantled. The muddy conditions in winter were the cause of some serious accidents. McCarthy has noted that 1927 was a particularly difficult year for those working on the railway. He provides a list of those unfortunate enough to be injured:

> A James Everett had a railway sleeper fall on him;
> A John O'Reilly was caught between two bogeys and had his leg fractured;
> A Thomas Kiely of Galway was run over by a railway bogey at Blackwater;
> A German mechanic Fritz Zaum was injured by a bogey at O'Briensbridge;
> A John Howard of Thurles was injured at Ardnacrusha when a set of rails fell on him.

Compensation for the victims of such accidents was minimal and sick pay nil.[11]

■ Bucket excavator and train in action.
Source: ESB Archives Photographic Collection.

■ Locomotive at work.
Source: ESB Archives Photographic Collection.

Late in 1927, McGilligan reported to the Dáil that there had been twelve fatalities and thirty-nine accidents in total. During the remainder of the construction phase of the project accidents on the railway system remained fairly common. The locals were not immune from some of the hazards of the railway. Thatched roofs were sometimes set on fire by passing trains; some of the locomotives were later fitted with spark arresters. Some young lads took to the practice of 'scutting': jumping on and off the trains as they traversed the lines. McCarthy also notes that some teenagers also amused themselves by changing the points on the rails, which sometimes caused derailments.

A fleet of a dozen or more Mannesmann–Mulag five-ton tractors was used for transport work between the harbour and locations on-site which could not be accessed by rail. Motor-boats, tugs and dredgers were also employed to transport material and plant from one bank of the Shannon to the other, and Lough Derg was also used in this manner to access the site locations at Portumna-Banagher. The capability of this fleet was impressive. One specialized tug, the *Neptunwerft*, for example, was used to convey a bucket dredger weighing approximately 35 tons across to Lough Derg. This particular tug had to be equipped with a 200-

horsepower engine. Coal and other fuel also had to be delivered to many site locations via the railway network.

In the latter half of 1927, the Board of Control, which had responsibility for ensuring that the project was completed on time, complained that the work was not being done to the agreed schedule. A serious row broke out between Siemens and McGilligan, which lasted for about nine months, and was only resolved after a series of high-level meetings. Several letters were exchanged between the House of Siemens, the Board of Control and the Minister's office.[12] Siemens had initially sought a six-month delay in the delivery of the contract, which the company stated was due to circumstances beyond its immediate control. In a letter to Campbell, Secretary of the Department of Industry and Commerce, Dr von Siemens pleaded for a six-month extension due to delays caused by a strike, three months of bad weather, scarcity of skilled labour, difficulty in obtaining work permits and lack of proper accommodation for some key German workers, the loss of the SS *Arabia* with a full cargo of equipment (including four locomotives and 50 km of railway track), a fire at the main stores in Ardnacrusha causing the loss of some critical stock, unanticipated earth conditions especially in the head-race canal, and the alteration of the original specification by transferring the site for the weir from O'Briensbridge to Parteen. It took several meetings to resolve how best to proceed but the government remained resolute, so it was Siemens who had eventually to give ground on the issue. Von Siemens took a decision to use more equipment and machinery rather than try to rely on extra staff; this included some additional locomotives and wagons. In some cases this simply made the existing railway lines more congested and actually slowed down progress. The major difficulties delaying the work were, however, resolved and sufficient work had been completed to allow the official opening ceremony to proceed on Monday 22 July 1929.

Writing in the *Railway Magazine* in August 1988, Hugh Dougherty recounts the story of David Flynn, who was only eighteen in 1926 but went on to play a key role in the day-to-day management of the Shannon Scheme railway system. Flynn's story is interesting in itself but it also provides us with an insight into life on the construction site. He was originally a pit engineer in the Sterlingshire coal mines before being made redundant. When the Germans decided, because of the low skill base in Ireland, to advertise in Scotland in 1925 for what we would describe in today's terms as technician positions, he did not hesitate in deciding to

Visit the Shannon Works!

See this Mighty Project in the making

Arrangements have been made with the Great Southern Railway to issue Return Tickets at Single Fares from all stations on its system to Limerick on week-days, available for return within three days including day of issue, from now on until the 29th of September inclusive.

Conducted Tours daily from the L D C premises
Sandfield Street, Limerick —
1st Tour leaves at 10.30 a.m., returning 1.30 p.m.
2nd   "   2.30 p.m.   6.30 p.m.
BUS FARE 4/- { Children Half-price }
Guide's services free.

Those not wishing to avail of these Conducted Tours should apply direct for a permit, giving date of proposed visit. Conducted Tours on SUNDAYS for large excursion parties ONLY.—

Apply to The ELECTRICITY SUPPLY BOARD
GUIDE BUREAU, STRAND BARRACKS, LIMERICK

■ *Source: History of the ESB,*
Manning & McDowell.

try his luck in Ardnacrusha. Flynn recalled: 'Thanks to my mechanical and electrical background in the pits, I was put in charge of hiring and firing Irish labour and also the railway. That included laying tracks on the 600mm system, erecting the overhead wires and poles for the electric line, and running the power station which was established for the duration of the contract.'[13]

Before being selected he had to pass a skills test in front of a German engineer to ensure he could operate all the equipment in the power station. Using only the German manuals as no English were available, he had to start up and switch on the generators which supplied the 550 Volts DC current for the railway: 'It was a miracle that I managed it, but I did and the line kept going with me in charge.'

Flynn, who returned to Scotland after the project was completed, subsequently worked in virtually every branch of engineering, acquiring en route three engineering degrees and patenting two engineering inventions.

Most of the locomotives were steam-driven, but in some sections of the network about ten electric locomotives were used for speed while the Scheme lasted. The railway network, although only a temporary phenomenon, left its mark on the local culture, as a *Limerick Leader* correspondent reported on 7 May 1927:

> Now the electric railway has in its insidious way got as far as Davidson's public house, and to my own knowledge still continues to frolic to and fro between there and Ardnacrusha, what was first a suspicion has in time become an accepted fact. I refer to the Limerick jarveys. I'm afraid that the present generation of Jehus of Limerick town are not living up to the traditions of their predecessors. In a previous article I went so far as to warn this German electric train of the risks it was running and of the almost certain chastisement it was going to receive at the hands of my friends the jarveys. But lo! It still continues to live and have its being, and the riders of these gallant steeds still continue to sit in somnolent ease on

■ Locomotive in transit.
Source: ESB Archives Photographic Collection.

the vehicles propelled by their still more somnolent equine companions. Thus have the mighty fallen. I'm afraid Geneva has a lot to answer for. Peace amongst all peoples is all right in its way, but there's such a thing as carrying it too far at the expense of losing some of the grand old fighting instincts of a hardy tribe. Even as Lir bewailed the loss of her daughters do I bewail the loss of the aggressive spirit amongst the nation's Jehus.[14]

Siemens was also the first to advocate the electrification of the Dublin suburban railway system. As part of its 1924 report on 'The Electrification of the Irish Free State',[15] Siemens investigated the possibility of electrifying the whole network of standard-gauge railways in Ireland. After a fairly exhaustive analysis they concluded it wouldn't be appropriate to proceed at that time because passenger traffic was still insufficient to justify the investment required. Siemens did, however, highlight the fact that the suburban line between Bray and Howth was a strong candidate for electrification at a later stage. Sixty years later the DART system came into operation; CIE, on the recommendation of Mott Hay & Anderson British Consulting Engineers, gave the contract to Siemens for the supply and installation of the overhead lines. In 2001 the electrified system was further extended to serve the growing populations in Greystones and Malahide.

Siemens did not waste much time in packing up the railway network lock, stock and barrel after the completion of the Shannon Scheme, leaving little or no evidence of the large rail network that had been constructed for its duration. The railway system was one of the most critical factors behind the success of the entire project.

Seán Keating, the Shannon Scheme and the Art of State-Building[1]

Andy Bielenberg

Seán Keating was the leading exponent in the Irish Free State of a new separatist identity in the visual domain. As Professor of Painting at the National College of Art from 1937, he provided formidable opposition to the emergence of modernism in Ireland, taking the view that modern art was destroying a carefully nurtured artistic tradition inherited from previous generations.[2] This conflict between realism and modernism, which gathered momentum from the 1930s, has to some extent defined the way his work has been received and assessed in the post-war era, making him an increasingly unfashionable subject in Irish art history. Sharpe, for example, describes his work as containing 'little more than soft-centred and belated romanticism, its stock in trade a world of heroic western peasants set in cardboard western landscapes', which reflected 'an ideology still immersed in Celtic twilight and the values of a vanished age'.[3] Fallon refers to him as one of 'the "official" academics', many of whom were 'reactionary followers of Orpen'.[4] The landscapes and portraits of this school, which also included McGonigal, Lamb and Touhy, in many instances reflected the preoccupations of cultural nationalism in the decades immediately before and after independence. The peasant scenes they painted, largely on the western seaboard, were increasingly viewed as banal by the modernists of subsequent decades.

■ Sean Keating on site at Ardnacrusha 1927. *Source: The Cashman Collection.*

While there is no denying that much of Keating's work was located in this genre (notably his Aran Islands paintings), or that he was highly traditional in his artistic technique and his attitude to modernism, there are aspects of his work in the inter-war years that deserve closer attention from art historians. His subject-matter in this period was not confined to western peasants and gunmen, and any serious appraisal of his work needs to go far beyond the same handful of paintings most Irish art history books select as examples of his art. Keating worked across the social spectrum, painting farmers, fishermen, hurlers, jockeys and tramps, apart from large numbers of portraits of the Irish middle class, from bishops and politicians to university dons. Despite introspective ethnic navel-gazing in works like 'Race of the Gael' and 'Cradle of the Race', much of his work in the inter-war years was unsentimental, and more attention needs to be given to the commercial commissions he undertook. Though Murray notes that the quality of his work was uneven, some being 'flawed, theatrical, and unconvincing', he acknowledges that at times Keating deserved the credit he received.

■ Building-site with Luffelbagger and wagon train.
Source: ESB Art Portfolio Catalogue.

His giant mural for the New York Trade Fair in 1939 displayed 'a zest for the modern world and a strong sense of design and abstract composition that was in no way retrogressive'.[5] Cullen also acknowledges the significance of Keating's work in its appropriate historical context, pointing out that it addresses the realities and preoccupations of the 1920s and '30s.[6] Keating was an important commentator on the changing world around him, an important source for those interested in appraising the attempts to construct a new national identity in the visual domain. This essay focuses on his efforts to record the progress of the Shannon Scheme, when the subject of his painting briefly intersected with the state-building project of the Cumann na nGaedhael government.

In the absence of a biography,[7] the best insights into Keating's academic training are to be found in Arnold's biography of Orpen (Keating's great teacher), and in Turpin's history of the Dublin Metropolitan School of Art (later the National

College of Art and Design), which describes the academic environment in which he subsequently worked. However, Keating was not strictly an academic painter, never accepting full-time employment in the art college, even when he became its professor of painting. He preferred not to be tied down by academic commitments, seeing himself as an artist first and a teacher second.[8] A greater share of Keating's income in the 1920s and '30s came from commissions. The nexus between the artist and his patrons is therefore critical in any appraisal of his work of this period. Like other academic artists, he undertook a large number of portraits, and he was also a beneficiary of the patronage of the Catholic Church. Keating also undertook a number of commissions for the state, such as large exhibitions and international trade fairs, the artwork for the Sweepstakes, as well as a host of private commissions, such as illustrations for books and journals, or commercial posters.[9]

The ecologically destructive transformation of the east-Clare landscape by huge machines, represented in Keating's work on the Shannon Scheme, provides a stark contrast to the serene West of Ireland landscape paintings of so many Irish-based artists in these years. Another notable aspect of these works is they are a very early example of the state's gradual emergence as a patron of the arts. Although this was not a formal commission from the outset, the ESB subsequently acquired most of Keating's paintings and drawings charting the progress of its major engineering works on the Shannon and subsequently at Poulaphouca.

Keating was born on 28 September 1889, at 11 Catherine Street, Limerick, the eldest of eleven children. He characterized his background as 'lower middle class'. His father and grandfather were listed by occupation as cork-cutters; his father also owned and ran a Limerick bakery for a number of years, before it went bankrupt. This was traumatic for the family, but the new owners of the bakery took his father on as a clerk.[10] In the words of the artist,

> his family members did not fit into the local ecclesiastical structure. Neither Mr nor Mrs Keating were members of the Confraternity. My father was a very uncommon phenomenon in that part of the world; he was a religious sceptic. I wouldn't say that he had his foot in both camps but he had his toe in both camps. He was a very liberal, very kind, very intelligent man. My mother was a good, ordinary, loving Irish mother of a big family doing her best. She was a women of taste with a little bit of

imagination, but I wouldn't say she had a powerful intellect. She had a great talent for mocking nicknames and malicious gossip. The whole town shared that characteristic.[11]

Keating's ambivalence about Limerick surfaced many years later, when he caused uproar after referring on television to the city of his youth as 'a medieval dung heap'. When asked in 1972 to explain his comment that the Limerick he grew up in 'stank', he willingly responded:

> I said it stank and that was not a figurative word. It literally did stink. There was an enormous dump on the south side of the docks behind Barrington's Bank where all the refuse of the town was blown out and blew around in the wind. The Corporation men set fire to the dump where they could and it smouldered all over the town. There was a tannery near St Mary's Abbey, it stank. Sewers emptied into the river. There was no regulations about slaughter houses. Food was exposed in the open air. Three or four bacon factories added to the flavour, and Nicholas Street, Mungret Street and down by the old Mall were sewers. It was so old and dilapidated it stank of decay. I knew where I was in Limerick by the smell.[12]

These vivid and sharply defined recollections of his youth illustrate the strong impression that the environment he lived in had on his memory. Neither was he flattering about his parents: 'They didn't know where they stood in the world, and what they were doing or why. They tumbled up and their children tumbled up and when the time came they tumbled into the grave.'[13]

Keating was educated at Leamy's National School, and as an older boy at St Munchin's. He seems to have done plenty of mitching around the Limerick docks, helping with odd jobs on ships. Apart from ships, he was fascinated by skilled work and machinery, anticipating his later interest in the Shannon Scheme. Taking time off school in his teenage years, he would go poaching. He recalled somewhat nostalgically in 1972 that

> I became a good poacher off the farm of friends in the mountains around Knocklisheen where I poached onto the adjoining lands. I was good at the

gun and grew very strong and robust. This lasted a considerable time until
one summer's morning after having had a very enjoyable night's poaching,
I came home to find nobody in the house and polished off the remains of
a leg of mutton and took out a box of cigars my father had given me – it
shows you the sort of liberal man my father was. I was about 17 or 18 at
the time. Then I had a sudden vision, like St Paul on the road to
Damascus. I saw myself as an idler on the wrong track, not pulling my
weight, not getting anywhere. I decided it would have to stop.[14]

Ultimately he was enrolled by his mother (who spotted his talent in drawing)
at the art classes at the Municipal Technical School, where Orpen, as an art
inspector, spotted him and persuaded him to move to the Dublin Metropolitan
School of Art in 1911. He received a scholarship of £40 a year, and over the next
years, Orpen became his great teacher; through him Keating imbibed the tradition
of European realism, most notably in the precision and directness that became a
strong feature of his work.[15]

Keating lived in immense poverty during his art school training.[16] In 1912 he
mustered the small sum required to accompany his fellow art students Harry
Clarke and Austin Molloy to Inisheer; this was the first of many trips to the Aran
Islands.[17] Although he was not the first artist to be inspired by the islands, no
other took such a sustained interest, and the islands featured strongly in much

■ Luffelbagger, wagon train and large group of figures in the foreground.
Source: ESB Art Portfolio Catalogue.

of his work over the next forty years. His Aran characters were hardy, mean, religious, cruel, humorous, brave and stoic; Keating was sympathetic to the self-sufficient way of life of the islanders. The Catholic middle class could readily identify with these rustic Aran images, which provided a powerful model for greater Irish cultural and political autonomy from Britain. The middle class in the new state provided a good market for such work, which is perhaps why they later became such a repetitive feature of Keating's output, and that of countless imitators.

Keating was singled out for special treatment by Orpen at the Dublin Metropolitan School of Art. One student recalled that 'he never said a word, or drew an illustrative line, for anybody except Keating'. Their relationship was more personal than merely that of master and pupil; Keating accompanied his teacher outside school hours, building up a close relationship, in 1915 he went to London to work as Orpen's assistant. During this period, Keating's Aran themes seem to have had some influence on Orpen's work. In the autumn of 1915 Keating brought back Aran clothing from the islands, and Orpen rang for his wife and children to come around, and they all dressed up and danced around the studio; the painting 'The Holy Well' grew out of that afternoon, with Keating modelling for two of the figures. These works marked a departure from his traditional realist style and content.[18] The use of allegory by Orpen, in 'The Holy Well', with unlikely configurations of public nudity, and his Rolls-Royce in the 'The Western Wedding', are indicative of Orpen's growing detachment from the Gaelic Revival. This was perhaps the most intense phase of co-operation between master and pupil, and Keating subsequently drew strongly from this experience, utilizing a similar allegorical approach in some of his more important paintings, such as 'Allegory' and 'Night Candles Are Burnt Out'.

Prior to the outset of the Easter Rising in 1916, background, religion and politics led to a parting of the ways between teacher and pupil, with Orpen remaining in London, the cosmopolitan centre of the United Kingdom and its empire, supporting the British war effort. Keating returned to Ireland, committed to Ireland's cultural and political renewal. He moved quickly through Dublin, taking another trip to the Aran Islands.[19] By immersing himself in island life, wearing island clothing and learning the Aran dialect of Irish, Keating believed he was touching the roots of 'national culture', giving it expression for the first time on canvas, reconstructing the essence of a pre-colonial Gaelic society from surviving fragments on the western seaboard.

Keating also joined the Gaelic League, and like much of his generation and class he was deeply influenced by its form of cultural nationalism, which remained a major inspiration in aspects of his work. The Gaelic League was particularly attractive to urban middle-class Catholics of his generation, and a large part of the nationalist revolutionary élite were members. Although he was a member of the radical Central Branch, O'Broin recalled that Keating had a more sceptical cast of mind than was prevalent within the organization.[20] For all his scepticism, however, he became more strongly nationalist between 1916 and the Civil War, and this influenced some of his work. Surviving correspondence demonstrates his willingness to exploit new opportunities to meet the growing demand for images of heroic gunmen in this period – but not at any cost. In relation to one such picture, he wrote to Estella Solomons[21] in 1917:

> Since I saw you in Grafton St this morning I have been thinking about this proposed raffle, and the more I think about it the less I like it. It

■ Excavator at work, Lubecker with stone wagon and steam shovel.
Source: Keating and Ardnacrusha, Exhibition at UCC Catalogue.

seems to me vulgar. Here is what I offer to you. Let the committee have the picture reproduced. I will give them the copyright and a very good photograph. There has not been a good Sinn Fein picture published yet and the very bad ones that have been published have sold like hot cakes. Let the reproductions be advertised in the Sinn Fein papers. ... if the reproductions could be published in America I will also give the American rights. The thing if properly done would be a source of income for months. Artists cannot be too careful of the prestige of their profession and to raffle a picture like a ham of bacon, or a ton of coals seems to me an objectionable proceeding.[22]

Keating had an address in Lower Gardiner Street, Dublin, and was clearly struggling to survive as an artist. He recalled many years later that 'for a year and a half in Gardiner Street I managed to keep alive selling some pictures at miserable prices. I sold 'The Fisherman and His Wife' which is now in the Municipal Gallery for £12 at that time. I wanted £15 but the buyer wouldn't give it.'[23] Keating accepted whatever work he could get, and by the end of 1918, with an address in 49 Rutland Street, he was undertaking portraits for £25.[24]

His prospects improved a little in 1918 when he was appointed as an assistant teacher at the Dublin Metropolitan School of Art. In the following year he married Mary Walsh (known as May), who was from a farming background in Eadestown, Co. Kildare; they met as a consequence of their common interest in the Irish language.[25] They both lived at 49 Rutland Street until 1921, when they moved out of the city to a cottage in Kilakee in the foothills of the Dublin mountains, moving two years later to Woodtown in Rathfarnham. May was more politically radical than Seán, working as secretary for Hanna Sheehy Skeffington, and also for Robert Childers Barton, Sinn Féin MP for West Wicklow in 1918 and one of the signatories of the Treaty.[26] Keating himself was a strong supporter of the Treaty; having friends on both sides, the Civil War disturbed him deeply.[27]

Keating's teaching income was very small in this period, amounting to only £132 by 1926,[28] so portraits and commissions remained an important component. The contract he made in 1934 with the Hospital's Trust Ltd, to take responsibility for all the artwork for the Sweepstakes, reveals that he received £2000, which was many times higher than his art college income; but this was probably exceptional. The proceeds from this were used to build his house, Áit an Chuain, at Rathfarnham in south County Dublin.[29]

Keating's first major commission was the Stations of the Cross in the chapel at Clongowes Wood College in 1919. By the end of 1921 this led to disputes with the Jesuits, who were unhappy with certain details. A suffering and bearded Christ bore Keating's visage, and Mary bore that of his wife, May. The priest in charge asked that Christ's face be altered. This was done, but Keating replicated the priest's face in his representation of Pontius Pilate.[30] The Jesuits were even more perturbed by his representation of the Hill of Calvary, which Keating defended impatiently, when the commission was almost complete:

> With regard to the much debated question of the 'Hill' of Calvary you adopt the no-hill theory; but how could I have known that when you made no objection to no. 12 nor to no. 4 – your favourite – in which the

level of the sky line in the background suggests an ascent even more forcibly than does the 'man hole' in no. 7 … It also served to overcome a technical difficulty which was this: I wanted where possible to let the Christ's head have the junction of the two arms of the cross for a background. This necessitated having the cross at a certain angle which cleared the ground where the Figure stood; when he was fallen the long line of the cross had to be deposed of by letting it disappear into the ground. An alternative such as you suggest would mean at this stage, more than merely taking a brush and painting something out and putting something else in, as one rubs out a figure on a blackboard. It would mean reconstructing my whole design – a thing I am not prepared to do. With regard to the glare of my colours, let me remind you that they are not intended for the close-range view nor for the light of my studio. I have before my mind while painting them the height and the light when in position on the walls of your chapel.[31]

This letter reveals some firmness in negotiation with a patron, and eagerness to finish a job he found less than inspiring. It also indicates that the commission was completed in his studio.

Keating was largely a studio painter who worked mainly in oil, charcoal and pencil, and occasionally watercolour. In Rathfarnham, an old grain mill beside his house served as a studio from the early 1930s onwards. He also had a studio at the art college in Dublin's city centre, which was more convenient to clients for portraits.[32] It is clear that he frequently worked from photographs, and in the 1930s he acquired a 16-mm camera, perhaps as a result of his close association with Robert Flaherty (who filmed *Man of Aran* in the 1930s). Keating was an early user of cine-colour film in Ireland, which he used sparingly as a notebook from which he could subsequently work back in the studio. As a result, some of his paintings in this period almost had the clarity of photographs.[33] However, a number of the paintings and drawings for the Shannon Scheme series were done on site, and it is to these that we shall now turn.

The Shannon Scheme became the central icon of industrial development and modernity for the new state, and the keystone of the state-building project in the economic sphere. The state strove to cultivate this image through the press, through

■ Ardnacrusha.
Source: By kind permission of Seamus Maguire.

guided tours of the site, through film footage and the production of postcards. It exploited the construction phase of the scheme as a visual image and monument, in Maguire's words, 'of a nation-state in the making'.[34] Keating's paintings and drawings were an added facet of this effort to bring the scheme into the public sphere, and to promote it as the flagship of nation-building and economic modernization. As such, it became part of a legitimating process for the government.

The radical proposal to harness the Shannon to generate electricity captured Keating's imagination: he was fascinated by machinery and technology. When work on the scheme got underway in the autumn of 1925, Keating returned to familiar settings close to his native city, to chart the transformation of the east-Clare landscape. The scheme was the most significant infrastructural investment made by the state in the inter-war years. It involved damming the river Shannon just above O'Briensbridge, carving a headrace through the landscape to a barrage and power station at Ardnacrusha (which had to be constructed), and a tailrace to return the water which had passed through the turbines back to the river just above Limerick.

■ Commencement of tailrace. Excavation work for canal and building of banks.
Source: ESB Art Portfolio Catalogue.

For a number of years it has been confidently asserted that Keating was commissioned in 1926 to execute a series of pictures illustrating the progress of the scheme.[35] The available evidence rules out this scenario. On 18 January 1927, when the scheme had been underway for well over a year, Keating wrote to one of his friends and mentors, Thomas Bodkin, from the School of Art: 'I am inviting some of the ministers and others interested in the Shannon Scheme to see some paintings and drawings which I made at Ardnacrusha in September. I shall be glad if you can come. Mr Cosgrave and the others have arranged to come to my room here at 3.30 on Thursday 20th but if that time does not suit you I shall be very happy to show the things to you at any time.'[36] This letter demonstrates conclusively that he had not been commissioned at this point, although he had succeeded in gaining an appointment with Cosgrave, who had at least shown sufficient interest to see the paintings. Keating's room in this instance was in the College, conveniently located in Kildare Street near the Dáil. It also indicates that a number of the paintings were complete, and that Keating was the proactive party looking for an opening, using his contact with Bodkin, an influential art critic, who had been a governor and guardian of the National Gallery of Ireland since 1917, and was just about to become its Director.

This meeting clearly did not lead to a sale. In 1927 and 1928 Keating exhibited eight of the Shannon Scheme series in the Royal Hibernian Academy, priced between £10 and £30.[37] In May 1929 the *Irish Times* records that Keating 'had spent many months at Limerick during the last two or three years painting scenes showing the progress of the Shannon project, which he intends to exhibit in London in the autumn'.[38] If the series were part of an official commission by either the state or the ESB, they would certainly not have been 'for sale' at the RHA or exhibited in London. Moreover, the best-known painting in the series, 'Night Candles Are Burnt Out', was sold to Oldham Art Gallery in April 1931 for the sum of £105.[39] Again, this suggests that the ESB had not yet purchased the series at this point.

■ Head working of a Connemara labourer. Working drawing of Michal McDonagh. *Source: ESB Art Portfolio Catalogue.*

It seems evident that it was his personal interest, notably the engineering and technical dimensions of the scheme, which drew Keating to the site. He knew an engineer, Laurence Kettle, who was helpful with introductions when the Scheme started. Laurence was the brother of Tom Kettle, who had been married to Hanna Sheehy Skeffington's sister.[40] It is possible that Keating made this connection through May's association with Hanna Sheehy Skeffington. Laurence Kettle was promoted to the board of the ESB in 1934; Keating had painted a portrait of him already by 1930. It is possible that the ESB acquired the Shannon Scheme series after Kettle's promotion, as a result of his influence. In any case, they acquired a number of paintings and drawings of the ESB's construction work at Poulaphouca, though it is not clear if those from the Shannon Scheme had already been acquired by the ESB at this point.

■ The timber gang, unloading timber on site.
Source: ESB Art Portfolio Catalogue.

What is clear is that in 1926 Keating was hard at work on the site at Ardnacrusha, sketching and painting as a freelance artist. During rain showers or blasting operations he took cover in a steel skip, which was always left lying close by to where he worked. After one of these blasts, he emerged from cover to find his easel and canvas flattened by flying rocks.[41] Workers from the Scheme (recently interviewed for the ESB Archive) remember him getting in the way when they undertook blasting operations at the site. Conditions for painting were not ideal, and the well-known photograph of Keating in wellingtons, hard at work with brush and palette in hand, is probably staged.

Negatives held by his son, Michael, indicate that photographs were used to record at least some of the Shannon Scheme images, which were then used in part to make up a drawing or painting back in his studio in Dublin. This is evident in 'Timber Gang', for example, a charcoal pencil drawing reproduced from a photograph (though the background differs from the photographic image). Others were done entirely or partially on site over a number of months.[42] Keating changed his style and medium to suit the circumstances he found himself in. This is why some (unusually for Keating) were done in watercolour, such as 'The Railway Yard' (dated 1926), a study of part of the large railway network which had to be constructed specially for the scheme. Another watercolour, 'The Canteen', records the bleak setting of one of the many points where food was prepared for the large workforce.

Some of the paintings record various engineering details, which Keating subsequently explained to his son, Michael (who became an engineer). Michael later explained some details in the painting 'Excavations for Headrace with Steam Shovel', for example, which had been passed on to him by his father. The

■ Railway yard at Ardnacrusha. Customised system to transport equipment and building material. *Source: ESB Art Portfolio Catalogue.*

hedgehog-like appearance of the rear end of the engine bay (to the left of the smokestack) on the steam-driven excavator was created by bundles of brushwood. The reason for this curious appendage, he explained, was that 'in the 1920s, track-mounted equipment was very slow, cumbersome and hard to manoeuvre. Excavators were not normally moved back for blasting. The back of the machine was protected by bundles of brushwood packed in under a specially provided grille as shown in the picture. The protective mat was turned towards the blast and the jib lowered. The flying rocks were (usually) stopped harmlessly by the brushwood.'[43] This gives some indication of Keating's eye for detail, and his deep interest in various problems confronting engineers working on the Scheme.

Much of Keating's significant output throughout his long life (which included some 500 paintings and drawings and around 100 portraits) focuses on the human face. In the Shannon Scheme series, by contrast, there is little attention to faces (with a few notable exceptions, such as the working drawing of a 'Connemara Labourer', 'Night Candles Are Burnt Out' and 'Der Ubermann'). Workers in most of the paintings and drawings are dwarfed by huge machines, toiling in a desiccated landscape. Keating faithfully and dramatically documents the devastating ecological impact of the machines. Most of the paintings focus on detailed operations within the site, with an emphasis on contour, bold strokes and strong colours. The painting 'Headrace Loking West', taken from the top of the barrage (providing an elevated view of the site and its setting), is particularly dramatic because it encompasses some of the surrounding landscape, making the ecological mess all the more apparent; no people can be discerned in this inhuman landscape. Its documentary accuracy and Keating's objective style are evident from one of the many photographs taken by Siemens of the site, which was clearly shot from the same spot at around the same time that the painting was in hand.[44] These photographs, which are now kept in the Siemens Museum in Munich, are perhaps the most comprehensive record of the progress of the Scheme.

Morrison's observation that Keating's Aran paintings focus predominantly on a male world[45] can be extended to his works on the Shannon Scheme. The female figure in the painting 'Der Ubermann' therefore stands out from the rest of the series. There is a degree of tension between them: she is well turned out and has clearly made an effort; he, with his back turned, is concerned only with the job at hand and the food she has brought. While the man's angle of vision and posture are consumed by the locale of his work, she looks sadly upwards, to the skyline where nature still prevails. She is somewhat alienated from the scene around her; from Keating's perspective this is not a place for women. The tension between the two lies in the contrast between the natural world (represented by the trees and sky) and the carved-up building site of the scheme. Keating was a keen observer of those engaged in the scheme; clearly he would have been familiar

■ Der Ubermann. Der Ubermann takes a break.
Source: ESB Art Portfolio Catalogue.

with the horrendous conditions they lived and worked in,[46] and the impact this had on personal relationships.

In 'Der Ubermann', Keating's realism comes out very strongly in his treatment of reflection in the water and rock face to the right of the couple, which are a good example of his immense skill in draughtsmanship and brushwork. This part of the painting relates closely to the right-hand side of 'Commencement of Tailrace', which contains the same details, including the treeline and the locomotive, but the sky remains unfinished in the latter painting. The centre and left-hand side of the painting do not correspond to the more faithful reproduction of the landscape in 'Commencement of Tailrace'. Instead, Keating resorts to a

■ View of the Power House with figures. *Source: ESB Art Portfolio Catalogue.*

common approach in his work, amalgamating different scenes from the site with sketched figures that were probably done in his studio; one sketch, of the women in this painting, has survived. A degree of realism is also evident in the detail of the different fibres of their clothing, and in the large piece of wood they are sitting on with its splintered edges. The more distant trees and sky are far less particular, almost impressionistic.

Some of these paintings were less precise, hurried, the paint applied thickly to the canvas. Many remained half finished, such as 'View of the Power House with Figures', in which squares are evident on the unfinished sections of the canvas, revealing the means by which scale and proportion were achieved. In this and in other unfinished works in the series (such as 'Commencement of Tailrace'), the means by which Keating primed the blank canvas (with a mixture of linseed oil, darkish brown raw umber and a few drops of turpentine) is apparent; in this he appears to follow the method used by Orpen.[47] The most significant feature of 'View of the Power House with Figures' is that it contains the genesis of a number of ideas which later appear in a more developed form in 'Night Candles Are Burnt Out', most notably the bridge and barrage in the background, but also the figure holding up the lamp to the left, and another in the group drinking.

The optimism with which both the state and Keating viewed the scheme must be seen in the context of the confidence of a European middle class in the liberating potential of technology and science during the inter-war years, and the

■ Night Candles Are Burnt Out.
Source: By kind permission of Oldham Art Gallery & Museums, England.

hope that it would ultimately solve most social problems. This view gave way to crushing disillusionment, following the horrors of the destructive application of technology during the Second World War, from the Holocaust to the atom bomb. The optimism of 'Night Candles Are Burnt Out (1928-9)' is partly wish-fulfilment, in which the artist places himself and his family as citizens centre stage; they now face a brighter future made possible by this huge state-driven engineering project. The images of youth and family, in the background and top right, are juxtaposed against the skeleton on the top left, hanging over a world which is to be swept away.

'Night Candles Are Burnt Out' – the title comes from *Romeo and Juliet* – provides a stark contrast to an earlier Keating painting, 'Allegory', which contains

■ The construction of the great dam.
Source: Irish Free State Official Handbook (1932).

many of the same characters. The military figures take centre stage in 'Allegory', as the other characters look helplessly on, with the big house of the old order in ruins in the background. In 'Night Candles', by contrast, the state replaces the estate as the dynamic locus of economic activity, and the future replaces the past in the background, with progress and development replacing death and fratricide. 'The dim candle light of surviving medievalism in Ireland', as Keating put it, '... is fading before the rising sun of scientific progress.'[48] At the time the reference to the priest, a marginal figure on the side wings in a squat position with the candle burning low, was considered to be somewhat subversive by critics who referred to this work as a 'problem picture'. The armoured car has a menacing presence, a reference to the recent military conflicts, but this is eclipsed by the Siemens excavator in the background, representing a more constructive use of technology. The businessman contractor is now the authority figure at the fulcrum of the work, sneering down contemptuously at the sole remaining gunmen. The dynamic actors in 'Allegory', the gunmen, have been replaced in 'Night Candles' by the businessmen and the family.[49] While Keating's perspective on the new social order is uncertain and sceptical in 'Allegory', in 'Night Candles' he becomes a willing propagandist for the new state. Keating explained to a journalist that 'the allegory represents the dawn of a new Ireland, and the death of the stage Irishman, who is seen hanging on one of the power standards in the corner of the picture'. One of the workers on the Scheme had been hanged for the robbery and murder of a German foreman in December 1928 (see Chapter 3) around the period the painting was executed. The artist also commented revealingly that 'anyone … would recognise the workmen as Connemara peasants'.[50] This group represents the stereotypical 'stage Irishman' he refers to – inebriated, passive, oblivious, part of a world which will be swept away by electrification and modernization. This is a far less sympathetic representation than his Aran subjects, who are purposeful, sober, and above all independent.

The available evidence indicates that Keating executed his Shannon Scheme paintings and drawings with a view towards a selling them to the state, an objective ultimately fulfilled when they were bought by the ESB some years later. Some of the series he undertook are not, however, in the possession of the ESB. 'The Construction of the Great Dam, Shannon Hydro-Electric Works, Ardnacrusha' was published in the *Irish Free State Official Handbook* in 1932. This book included other examples of Irish industrial art, notably Harry Kernoff's drawings of the Guinness Brewery and the locomotive works at Inchicore. However, the dominant subject-matter of the art work in this production was landscape and antiquity, revealing the official view of what constituted 'national art'.[51]

Keating subsequently undertook a range of work centred on major industrial and engineering projects including the ESB scheme at Poulaphouca, wartime turf production at Clonsast and the Boyne Road Cement Factory, often using contacts with engineers he had made on the Shannon Scheme.[52] These works documented various aspects of state intervention in Irish economic development. If we can judge by the number of paintings and drawings he undertook of the Shannon Scheme, and the greater effort he invested in this project relative to his other economic themes, it is evident that he attached particular importance to it.

Keating was perhaps more successful than any other Irish artist in winning commissions during the inter-war years from a range of patrons, including the state. The subject-matter he focused on in the 1920s and '30s reflected the populist nationalist ethos of the Catholic middle-class élite, who were the main consumers of art in the new state and the main subjects of Keating's portraits. Clearly his brand of nationalism appealed to those newly in power, and he produced art which had a legitimating function for them. In various power struggles within the School of Art in the 1930s, Keating used his status as a 'national painter' with government officials and de Valera to defend his position against those who, he perceived, were trying to undermine his position. He wished to make the school 'active, national and productive', as opposed to 'obsolete, non-Gaelic and non-productive'.[53]

Keating clearly shared a common view among nationalists that the old regime was characterized by a high degree of economic, political and cultural inertia, and that hopes for the future development lay in some kind of fusion of a dynamic 'Gaelic culture' with a greater degree of technocratic state intervention in the economic sphere. The hopes for such a fusion of ideas are clearly evident in an article in the *New York Times Magazine*:

> ... it is by no means so easy to forecast the reactions of this departure upon Irish life as it is lived today. Will it mean in the long run the emergence of a new type of Irishman, alert to apply to his own purpose every modern discovery and every improved method, yet cherishing at the same time the ideals of the legendary past and drawing his mental sustenance from Gaelic culture? Hitherto it has been only in politics that Irishmen have been revolutionaries; in everything else they are the most resolute and unbending conservatives in Europe. It may be that Gaelic, backed by electrical power, will provide an explosive mixture strong enough to smash the old moulds and radically transform Irish mentality.[54]

For Keating and other members of the Gaelic League (the most influential component of cultural nationalism prior to independence), the locales within Irish society from which inspiration could be drawn were those of the western seaboard, where it was imagined something of a pre-colonial golden age had survived. The focus of a number of nationalist painters on the west of Ireland had parallels in the literary culture emerging from the Blasket Islands of the south-west in the 1930s and in the way in which folklore was used in the process of nation-building. Ó'Giolláin notes that folklore collectors worked among those sections of the population most removed from metropolitan culture; the urban middle class idealized these sections of the population and the landscapes they lived in, not only in Ireland, but also in Finland, the United States, Austria and Hungary, among other places.[55]

But there was an element of incongruity between Keating's work on Shannon Scheme, which charted the efforts to transform a predominantly agrarian society into a modern industrialized nation, and his focus on the Aran Islands, one of the least developed parts of the country. This conflict was already evident within the different strands of cultural nationalism prior to independence, in the contrast between the objectives of the co-operative movement to introduce new technologies and modernize the dairy industry, and, on the other hand, those strands within cultural nationalism which viewed the west of Ireland as the essence of Gaelic authenticity. During the 1950s this became evident in the polarity established by the economic imperatives of Lemass, concerned with future development, and de Valera's vision of a rural arcadia, firmly rooted in the past. Seán Keating's work in the inter-war years encapsulates this inherent tension between past and future, starkly apparent in the conflicting aspirations of the revolutionary generation of a middle class in the new state of which he was part. His preoccupation with tradition is evident in his Aran work, while the allure of modernity is best exemplified by his representations of the Shannon Scheme.

Some Notable Features of the Design and Operational History of Ardnacrusha since 1929

Bob Cullen

The power station at Ardnacrusha was initially designed to exploit the extensive catchment area of the Shannon. The total storage of the Shannon system is approximately 600 million tons. The average flow of the river at Killaloe is 180 tons per second, but this can vary from 10 to 15 tons per second in dry summers to over 700 tons per second in a major flood. The headrace and power station can discharge 400 tons of water per second at maximum load. The conventional design of a large storage basin formed by a high dam with a power station at its foot was not possible due to the topography of the area. Instead the design involved the construction of a smaller dam or weir on the river upstream of the village of O'Briensbridge, five kilometres south of the town of Killaloe. A canal was then constructed from the weir to the site of the power station at Ardnacrusha some 12.6 kilometres away. The canal follows the slope of the hills to minimize the amount of material required for the embankments on either side. At Ardnacrusha, the canal terminates in a 30-metre high dam through which the 6-metre diameter penstocks feed the water to the turbines in the power station at the foot of the dam. The water emerging from the power station is then carried by way of a tailrace canal, 2.4 kilometres long, back to the river Shannon, some 3 kilometres upstream of Limerick.

The generating plant at Ardnacrusha is composed of three vertical-shaft Francis turbo-generators (installed in 1929) and one vertical-shaft Kaplan turbo-generator

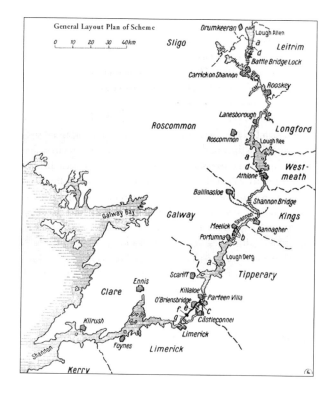

General Layout Plan of Scheme

0 10 20 30 40km

Drumkeeran
Lough Allen
Sligo
Leitrim
Battle Bridge Lock
Carrick on Shannon
Rooskey
Lanesborough
Roscommon
Longford
Roscommon
Lough Ree
West-meath
Athlone
Ballinasloe
Shannon Bridge
Galway Bay
Galway
Kings
Meelick
Bannagher
Portumna
Lough Derg
Scariff
Tipperary
Ennis
Clare
Killaloe
O'Briensbridge
Parteen Villa
Kilrush
Castleconnel
Limerick
Foynes
Limerick
Shannon
Kerry

■ *Source: The Shannon Hydro-Electric Scheme, Siemens-Schuckert (1930).*

(installed in 1934) operating under an average head of 28.5 metres. The 85 MW of generating plant in Ardnacrusha was adequate to meet the electricity demand of the entire country in the early years. Sometimes, especially at night in winter, water had to be wasted because the total system demand was so small. Since about 1950 it has been possible to avail of the full output, which equates to about 332 thousand MW per year. Ardnacrusha generates at 10.5 kilovolts (kV), but this is transformed to 40 kV for local distribution and to 110 kV for long-distance transmission.

Parteen Weir controls the flow of water from the Shannon into both the head-race and the old river channel. There are six sluice gates on the old river outlet and three sluice gates and a navigation gate on the canal outlet. A flow of 10 tons per second is allowed down the old river for fishery and conservation purposes. Apart from this flow, all available water up to the full station capacity is discharged down the headrace canal. In major floods, when the flow in the river exceeds 400 tons per second, the excess is released down the old river channel.

Table 1 Technical Particulars

Catchment area: 10,400 km²

Average annual rainfall 1,000 mm

Average annual flow 180.0m³/sec

Average head 28.3m

Turbines	1	2	3	4
Type	Francis	Francis	Francis	Kaplan
Rated H.P.	34,000	30,000	30,000	30,000
R.P.M.	150	150	150	167
Year com.	1929	1929	1929	1934
Maker	Escher Wyss	Voith	Voith	Voith

Alternators	1	2	3	4
3 phase, 50 cycle				
Nor. Rating (kVA)	30,000	30,000	30,000	30,000
Power Factor	0.7	0.7	0.7	0.9
Voltage	10,500	10,500	10,500	10,500
Maker	S.S.W.	S.S.W.	S.S.W.	S.S.W.

Weir: 4 double roller gates 10m wide

2 single roller gates each 18m wide.

Head Race: Length 12.8 km. Capacity 400m³/sec.

Tail Race: Length 2.4 km

Transformers Name	Maker	Capacity	Voltage Ratio
T101 T102 T103	S.S.W.	30,000kVA	11,000/112,300
T104	S.S.W.	30,000kVA	10,500/112,000
T141	A.E.G.	31,500kVA	110,000/40,887
T41	A.S.E.A.	8,000kVA	11,282/ 43,365
T42 T43	S.S. W.	8,000kVA	11,000/43,365
T44	S.S.W.	8,000kVA	11,000/42,315
ST11 ST12	A.E.G.	800kVA	10,500/397,000

Arc Suppression Coils		
100 ASC	S.S.W.	120A
40 ASC1 & 40ASC2	A.S.E.A.	80A

Sources: ESB Archive Dublin; 'The Story of ESB', ESB PR document.

Ardnacrusha became the headquarters of ESB upon its inception in 1929.[1] The decision as to which power stations would supply the demand at any time was made by the control-room staff at Ardnacrusha and they retained this function until the load despatch office was established in Dublin in 1954.[2] Initially, two Swedish engineers, on loan from the Swedish Board of Waterfalls, were appointed. The Chief Operation Officer for ESB was Mr T. Strand, while Mr E. Berggren was appointed Station Superintendent at Ardnacrusha.[3] Under their direction and supervision, it was determined that Irish staff should be trained up to take over. The first Irish Station Superintendent, Alexander Cooney, was appointed on 1 November 1931 and the Swedish Chief Operation Engineer left in 1932.[4]

■ Control room at Ardnacrusha. *Source: ESB Archives Photographic Collection.*

Since that time, most positions in Ardnacrusha have been filled by Irish personnel, although there have always been a number of non-nationals, in addition to non-Clare/Limerick personnel, employed. Units 2 & 3 at Ardnacrusha were transferred to the ESB on 21 October 1929 and were put into commercial operation on 24 October 1929. On that date the supply to what was called the 'Leinster Loop' was made available through the 110kV transmission line to Inchicore. This supplied a number of towns in Leinster and Munster. Unit 1 was transferred to ESB on 11 November 1929. By the end of that year the maximum network load was 4.5 MW.[5]

On 13 January 1930 Ardnacrusha was synchronized with the Pigeon House power station in Dublin and both operated in parallel until 25 January 1930, when Pigeon House was closed down. From that date, supply for Dublin City and most of the suburbs was from Ardnacrusha. Fords in Cork received a supply from Ardnacrusha for the first time in February 1930. From small beginnings, load demand increased significantly as more towns were gradually connected to the network and small utilities were closed down.

In 1931 Ardnacrusha generated 96 per cent of the total national generation. The remaining 4 per cent was by local utilities, which had not yet been taken over by ESB.

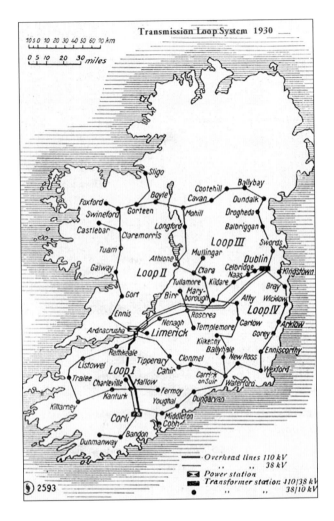

Transmission Loop System 1930

Loop III
Loop II
Loop IV
Loop I

Overhead lines 110 kV
"   "   38 kV
Power station
Transformer station 110/38 kV
●   "   38/10 kV

■ *Source: The Shannon Hydro-Electric Scheme, Siemens-Schuckert (1930).*

The early 1930s saw a number of droughts. The Pigeon House power station was brought back into commission to alleviate the problem. The demand for electricity continued to increase, and despite the droughts a fourth unit was commissioned at Ardnacrusha in 1934. This unit had a Kaplan turbine, the other three being Francis turbines. Kaplan technology had not been developed sufficiently to install them in the 1920s, during the initial construction phase. If Ardnacrusha had been built in the 1930s (or later), then all turbines would have been of the Kaplan design. This marked a technical breakthrough in the area of hydropower in global terms, since this was the first Kaplan turbine in the world

■ Spiral casings for the Francis turbines.
Source: Siemens Progress on the Shannon Scheme, Number 2, November 1928.

for a head exceeding 30m. On commissioning, the machine met all expectations. It demonstrated the leading position of German hydro-turbine production at the time, which was based both on theoretical knowledge and on the results of detailed scientific and technical experiments in a purpose-equipped factory laboratory. Schoen observes:

> The acceptance tests at Ardnacrusha in March 1934 gave very good results; the guarantee values were significantly exceeded. The turbine operation was excellent. Its design had been subject to extensive model investigations in the test facilities of the manufacturers (in Hermaringen), and the successful results emphasized the importance of such modern test laboratories … [He added:] The manufacturers selected a seven-blade design for the rotor

of the Shannon Kaplan turbine; this number of blades was considered necessary for safety reasons. To counter the risk of cavitation on the rotor in Ardnacrusha, the tangential blade lengths were made particularly large, in addition to having the high number of blades; the blades partially over-lapped, so that the rotor was no longer 'transparent'. In this way, the hydraulic loading (and thus the susceptibility to cavitation) was reduced. Additionally, the especially resistive material 13% chrome steel was used for the blades. The excellence of the construction of the fourth Shannon turbine was demonstrated by its extraordinarily low vibration manifestations, and by the almost complete absence of cavitation damage to be observed in later inspections, unlike with the three Francis turbines.[6]

To enable the waters of the Shannon to be utilized more effectively the river was deepened above Killaloe and the Navigation Weir at Killaloe was removed. The bridge between Killaloe and Ballina had a steel span installed on the Tipperary side. This was capable of being raised to permit navigation, if and when the level of Lough Derg was raised to the proposed final development level. The sluices at the outlet of Lough Allen were replaced by new ones with a lower sill level and the outlet channel deepened. The old navigation canal from Acres Lake was dammed and navigation into, or out of, Lough Allen was not to be restored until the last decade of the twentieth century. This turned out to be the final devel-opment of Ardnacrusha and of the Shannon. Although it was initially planned to have six turbine/generator units as the final development of the Scheme, the decision was taken to limit the development to four, as there was insufficient water available to justify six units economically. Parteen Weir, the intake and tailrace canals and the dam at Ardnacrusha are all designed to accommodate six turbine/gen-erator units. The two spare openings in the dam at Ardnacrusha remain blocked up and the level in the headrace is one metre lower than the canal's capability. The embankments north of Parteen Weir were not raised to final development level.

Almost from the start, slips of the embankment material and leaks through the embankment occurred. The embankments are earthen throughout, and they were constructed with whatever material was available locally. At a peak in 1933–5, just over 150 men were employed grouting and stemming leaks and seepages that had arisen in the headrace embankments. Not all leaks have been successfully sealed and some continue to the present day.

■ Two Buckauer multiple bucket excavators working on the embankment near O'Briensbridge.
Source: Siemens Progress on the Shannon Scheme, Number 5, February 1927.

The design of the generator cooling systems was found to be faulty and new cooling systems were installed in the mid '30s. However, damage had occurred to the generator stator cores and they had to be repaired at the end of the decade. Another design difficulty emerged in the early years in connection with turbine No. 1., which was suffering cavitation damage. Following consultations with the manufacturers Escher Wyss, a new turbine was installed in 1933 and its acceptance tests were carried out in 1937. The results obtained were 'very satisfactory in every respect and have not only fulfilled, but certainly exceeded the expectations'.[7] It was to be 1993 before that turbine, or indeed any of the other turbines installed in 1929 and 1934, were removed from their positions.

The positioning of a weir, which is in reality a dam at Parteen, and the diversion of most of the waters of the river Shannon through Ardnacrusha affected the migrating salmon and eels. Provision was made for the passage of fish at Parteen but not at Ardnacrusha. The nineteenth-century 'Queen's Gap Act' required that 'provision be made for the passage of fish in all dams, weirs, etc. constructed on all natural rivers and watercourses'. The Ardnacrusha dam, being on a man-made watercourse, was deemed not to require a fish-pass. However, the salmon had a tendency to try to go up the canal, rather than the river to Castleconnel and

Parteen Weir, and various methods were employed to direct the salmon up the river. These included an electric barrier at the mouth of the tailrace. All were unsuccessful. The construction of Parteen Weir and the diversion of most of the waters of the Shannon through Ardnacrusha significantly affected the livelihood of the Abbey fishermen. These fishermen plied their narrow fishing cots between Limerick City and the Falls at Doonass and exercised their ancient skill of snap net fishing. In 1932 they took on the army, police and water bailiffs in a series

■ Transport of bucket excavator on two barges. *Source: Siemens Progress on the Shannon, Number 11, August 1927.*

of engagements which have since been known as the Battle of the Tailrace. The conclusion was inevitable. Compensation was eventually accepted and the Abbey fishermen became a footnote in history.[8]

In 1935 the Shannon Fisheries were transferred to ESB. To conserve the declining stock level of salmon, no commercial fishing was allowed between 1935 and 1941. It is interesting to note that Patrick McGilligan and Sean Lemass, both of whom were Ministers for Industry and Commerce, emphatically stated the principle that in the case of a clash of interests, the interests of the electricity works were to predominate over those of the fishery owners. (All attempts to divert the salmon from the tailrace failed and it was decided in the mid '50s to construct a Borland-type fish lift to permit the salmon to pass the dam at Ardnacrusha. Construction of the lift was completed in 1959. Simultaneously, a salmon hatchery was built at Parteen Weir.)

Ardnacrusha luckily had no 'fuel' problems during the 1940s. The plant performed well and little trouble was experienced until January 1948. Its annual

■ Fish hatchery, Parteen. *Source: ESB Public Relations Brochure.*

contribution to national demand during the war varied between a low of 53 per cent and a high of 71 per cent of units generated. For ESB staff the war was also a time of confidence-building as the main contractor, Siemens-Schuckert, could no longer help during overhauls or with technical problems. The ESB's own staff proved to themselves and others that they were capable of operating and maintaining generating stations. Reliance on foreign expertise diminished from then.

Because of the war spare transformers were not available for the national network. The building that had housed the temporary power station for the construction of Ardnacrusha was converted to set up a transformer repair shop. This was done from scratch, with little knowledge of transformer repair. It carried ESB and Ireland through the war years and eventually became a significant addition to ESB's ability to maintain the networks. Transformer coils were initially wound by hand. Up to the 1990s about 46 different makes had been repaired at Ardnacrusha. The repair shop has now passed its heyday, although there is still the expertise and facility to repair a number of transformers every year. Spares for very old transformers are still available in Ardnacrusha despite the best efforts of modern management practices and accountancy principles to reduce stock holdings.

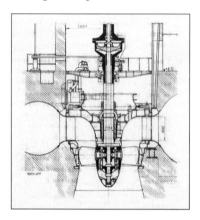

■ Diagram of Kaplan turbine.
Source: Siemens Archives.

In January 1945 a CIE barge with a cargo of cement going upstream had to tie up to a tree as it was unable to make headway against the flow. The crew adjourned to the nearby village for sustenance. When they returned the barge was at the bottom of the tailrace. Instead of the tide going out, as happens at coastal piers, the turbines had come off load. This lowered the water level in the tailrace; the rope held the barge until it broke. The barge was not raised until 1954.

The headrace canal, being man-made, was an obstacle to the natural drainage of the land west of the canal. To allow this land to continue to drain, a number of culverts or drainage pipes were installed under the headrace. In July 1947 50mm of rain fell very locally in about two hours. The water level, local to one of the culverts, rose 15m, flooding the local area. No rainfall was experienced at the power station or anywhere near that local area. ESB was taken to the High Court but was successful in its defence. The incident showed that extremely high rainfall could occur very locally and work had to be done to help alleviate the effects of such occurrences. A slip occurred on the eastern embankment north of Parteen Weir, i.e. the Fort Henry Embankment. This slippage actually happened on the dry side, or outside, of the embankment. This was the nearest thing to an embankment breach over the seventy-plus years of operation of the Shannon Scheme.

By the start of the 1950s it was time to improve conditions at Ardnacrusha, taking advantage of improving technology and management practices. The '50s

■ Fish pass at Ardnacrusha.
Source: ESB Public Relations Brochure.

saw an extension to the workshops and the station building. The latter not only accommodated additional switchgear for the 38kV network but also a conference room and a reception area for visitors.

Following a bad flood in 1954, the government commissioned Louis Rydell, an engineer of the United States Army, to advise 'on the possibility of dealing effectively and permanently with the periodic flooding in the Shannon Valley'. His final report was published in 1956. In it he stated: 'The problem of Shannon River flooding has been the subject of much study over the past 150 years. Because of the flat terrain through which the river flows, the almost imperceptible gradient of the stream with its series of lakes and connecting channels, and because of the large volume and long duration of flooding, no simple or obvious solution has heretofore been found – nor has the writer now found one.'

The Rydell Report had recommended that further investigations be carried out into the question of flood control, and in 1961 the ESB and OPW issued their report on the 'Shannon Flood Problem'. They proposed two schemes: the 'Full Relief Scheme' and the 'Summer Relief Scheme'. The 'Full Relief Scheme' was judged to involve expenditure which would be incommensurate with the benefits achieved. The 'Summer Relief Scheme' would give relief from most spring, summer and autumn floods and substantially reduce the magnitude and duration of winter floods. Further detailed field investigations and an agricultural survey were recommended. Neither scheme was implemented nor were any further investigations carried out. At Ardnacrusha, the generators were rewound on Units 1, 2 and 3 in the early '60s.

A railway line was constructed by Siemens-Schuckert to transport materials from Limerick docks and from Dublin to the power station. It continued in use to a limited degree until the '60s, when it was last used in the making of the film *Guns in the Heather*. During the Second World War CIE borrowed the rails. At the war's end they were replaced with rails taken from those laid by the Germans in the Channel Islands. The rails and sleepers were finally taken up in the '90s and donated to the West Clare Railway Preservation Group.

At Parteen Weir there was a requirement to discharge a minimum flow of water down the Shannon river, through Castleconnel, to Limerick. This flow was utilized in 1979 to generate electricity by the installation of a 600kW mini-hydro unit. In 1979 there was another embankment slip on the Fort Henry embankment. This time it was on the waterside and again was very significant. Its cause was put down to 'drawing down', or lowering, the water level in the lake too quickly. The level of water in Lough Derg had to be lowered significantly to permit repair and it was the last time that navigation was prohibited on the lake. The slip in 1979 led to the appointment of the Swedish consultancy firm, SWECO, to investigate comprehensively the stability of all the Shannon embankments.

■ Ardnacrusha. *Source: ESB Archives Photographic Collection.*

■ Intake and weir, Ardnacrusha. *Source: ESB Archives Photographic Collection.*

The SWECO recommendations, as they became known, were implemented between 1982 and 1986. This brought the condition of the embankments up to modern standards.

Simultaneously, the ESB carried out a review of its dam supervision and maintenance procedures. This was completed in 1987 with the appointment of an External Dam Safety Committee under the chairmanship of Guntram Innerhoffer and with the appointment of a nominated dam-supervising engineer. The chairman of the External Dam Safety Committee reports directly to the Chief Executive of ESB. The Committee carries out reviews or inspections of differing depths annually, five-yearly and ten-yearly. By this ESB ensures that its dams and embankments are kept up to best modern international standards in the absence of any national standards or regulation. A roadway replaced the local railway to the station in 1980. Before the installation of the roadway, to get equipment that was less than 32 tons into or out of the workshop, a winch was used to lower it on tracks. This winch and associated equipment was finally removed in the '90s.

Ardnacrusha's reduction in importance to national electricity generation meant that the ESB could reconsider its operating regime on the Shannon. In agreement with various interests, ESB now endeavours to maintain the Shan-non at a water level suitable for the leisure industry during the tourist season and as low as possible in the off season to mitigate the effect of floods. The use of Lough Allen for strategic water storage was no longer necessary and ESB entered into an agreement with local community interests to modify its exploitation.

At the end of the '80s and into the early '90s a number of sinkholes started appearing, depressions up to a metre in depth near the embankments. A study of the cause of these indicated that they were in a limestone area and subject to 'Karst' conditions. This meant that small particles were being carried away by leakage water and holes created underground. Eventually the overburden collapsed and sinkholes appeared. Extensive grouting of the embankments and surrounding ground was carried out and the problem has not re-occurred.

The '90s saw the refurbishment of Ardnacrusha after more than sixty years of operation. The mechanical and electrical plant was essentially the same as had been installed in 1929 and 1934; while the generating plant had been well maintained, there were signs of age. Additionally, the electrical system did not meet modern safety standards and spares were becoming difficult to obtain. A decision was taken to refurbish completely the electrical system and make the plant suitable for remote control. New unit transformers were installed. Three of the turbines were replaced with more modern ones, which individually can produce a greater output: Unit 3's turbine was not replaced and was not removed. The total output of the stations was increased to 91 MW. A new control room was built, cantilevered out through the end wall. Its design was the result of a competition for fourth-year architectural students in Bolton Street, Dublin. The old control room is being maintained as part of Ireland's industrial heritage, as are the original transformers and a significant amount of the original plant.

As part of the Shannon Scheme, four bridges were built across the headrace and tailrace. They are still in ESB's ownership. A complete study of these bridges was carried out and they were modified to modern standards. Additionally the refurbishment of all intake gates, spillway gates and navigation lock gates at Parteen Weir and Ardnacrusha began. The OPW built new navigation locks at Drumshambo,

Co. Leitrim, and re-opened navigation into Lough Allen. This necessitated another revision to the operating regime at Lough Allen. In 1996 Ardnacrusha became the first power station in the world to achieve ISO 9002 – an award from the International Organization for Standardization – for its management system. The achievement of the ISO 9002 was as a result of a project as part of a supervisory management-training programme.

Ardnacrusha and the Shannon river had unwelcome visitors in the '90s. Zebra mussels entered the waterway and have found their way through the river and canals and are now throughout the catchment. Zebra mussels grow rapidly, and while they have the advantage of helping to clean the water, they also remove the nutrients from the water and block up intake and discharge pipes. When they die off collectively there is a significant release of toxins.

The '90s also saw three of the worst floods of the century: in February 1990, in the winter of 1994/1995, and in December 2000. This last flood, like its predecessor in 1954, resulted in government seeking recommendations. A Sub-Committee of the Joint Committee on Public Enterprise and Transport considered issues relating to the management of the river Shannon and their final report is awaited.

The construction of Ardnacrusha changed the environment of the Shannon catchment downstream of Parteen Weir. That part of the river no longer has the same flows as it had prior to the Shannon Scheme. This has meant considerable development on what were previously substantial flood plains. Again, some of the lands east of the Shannon upstream of Parteen Weir and west of the Shannon north of Portumna have been drained for over seventy years. It is very unlikely that the Shannon would be returned to its pre-Scheme condition.

Now that the twenty-first century has begun, what is the likely future for Ardnacrusha? The power station generates 'green electricity': the energy source is renewable, and in its passage through the power station it is unchanged. The hydropower of the Shannon, as harnessed at Ardnacrusha, remains important to the system as a rapidly available source of peak power and for cover in cases of emergency or sudden breakdown elsewhere.

Ardnacrusha performed exceptionally well throughout the twentieth century. Like all plants, it had teething-problems but once solved the plant and structures proved very reliable. Much has been written about the design and construction phase of the Shannon Scheme in this book, but without the ESB staff who operated and maintained the plant and structures since it was first commissioned down to the present, Ardnacrusha would not be the monument it is today to the vision of those that designed and built it. At the start the day staff numbered one hundred and fifty, with large numbers taken on for seasonal work. With the passing years numbers dropped as machinery and technology made work less labour-intensive. By the end of the century there were sixty-eight staff employed at Ardnacrusha. There was no operating personnel at Parteen Weir and only one per shift at Ardnacrusha. The plant and structures have been maintained in excellent condition and where necessary brought up to modern standards.

The station still makes a contribution, but this declined from 96 per cent of national generation in 1931 to only 1.5 per cent of the total by 2000,[9] as a number of new stations were pressed into service to meet massive growth in demand for electricity in the intervening years and the economy became more industrialized and urbanized. Despite this transformation, Ardnacrusha continues to have special significance as the birthplace of the ESB. The origins of the organization were intimately connected with developments on the Shannon Scheme, and those who work within it are still aware of this important feature of its history, which marked a turning-point in the economic and political history of the state, copper-fastening the political revolution that preceded it.

Notes

■ **Delany, 'McLaughlin, the Genesis of the Shannon Scheme and the ESB'**

1. P. Duffy, 'Rishworth, McLaughlin and the Shannon Scheme' (unpublished paper presented to Cumann Ceimithe na Gaillimhe for the Christy Townley Biennial Lecture on 31 October 2001).
2. T.A. McLaughlin, 'How I Thought of the Shannon Scheme', RTE script 1938, ESB Archive, Dublin.
3. Ibid.
4. R. Kane, 'Industrial Resources of Ireland', paper published under the auspices of the RDS (1844).
5. Shannon Water & Electric Power Act (1901). Private Act passed by parliament in London.
6. W. Tatlow, 'S.F. Dicks' Proposal based on fall at Doonas', *Trans. Inst. Civil Engineers of Ireland* (hereafter TICEI), vol. 45 (1902), p. 81.
7. T. Stevens, 'The Liffey Scheme Dublin 1923', *Report on The Water Power Resources of Ireland & The Shannon Scheme in true Perspective* (Dublin 1926).
8. J. Crowley & Partners, 'Report on National Electricity Supply Scheme', details contained in Experts' Report.
9. J. Chaloner Smith, 'Notes Upon the Average Volume flow ... deducted from gaugings on the River Shannon at Killaloe', *Trans. Inst. Civil Engineers of Ireland,* vol. 45 (1920), pp. 41–118.
10. P. Duffy, 'Rishworth, McLaughlin and the Shannon Scheme', op. cit. 'Some countries have taken this principle of utilisation of home resources in power as an essential one to be adhered to even if imported fuel would give power somewhat cheaper. We in Ireland do not find it necessary to take this attitude because in the majority of cases, even in outlying towns and villages, we will find it cheaper to utilise power there derived from water. We may then approach the matter from a narrow commercial view-point, and ask what equivalent in fuel value will the partial development of the River Shannon produce for us at home. The Coal Conservation committee reported some years back that in Great Britain on an average of 5lbs. of coal were required to produce one horse power hour of energy. We may take this as a fair average for conditions today. The Shannon Scheme under Partial Development will produce 288 million units (MW) in a year of average rainfall. On the above basis this is the equivalent in energy to 860,000 tons of coal. Reckoning coal at an average of thirty shillings a ton throughout the Free State this is equivalent in money to ir£1,290,000. In this first stage of the Shannon Scheme, therefore we have the possibility of producing at home the equivalent of ir£1,290,000 worth of present day imports. If we capitalise this sum @ 5 per cent we arrive at ir£25,800,000. The Shannon Scheme, in its partial development, will cost ir£5,200,000. Surely it is good business to invest a capital sum of ir£5,000,000 to get the equivalent of a capital investment of ir£26,000,000' (T.A. McLaughlin, *The Shannon Scheme Considered in its National Economic Aspect* [Dublin 1924]).
11. ESB Archive, Dublin; McLaughlin, op. cit.
12. McLaughlin, 'How I Thought of the Shannon Scheme', op. cit.
13. Irish Government White Paper on Proposals for the Development of the Shannon Scheme (1924).
14. G. O'Beirne, *History of Siemens in Ireland 1925–2000* (Dublin 2000), p. 75.
15. M. Manning, M McDowell, *History of ESB* (Dublin 1984), pp. 87–8.

16. McLaughlin, 'The First Five Years of ESB', *Engineers Journal*, vol. 21, no. 16 (1968).
17. *Irish Press*, 16/11/1963. *Irish Independent*, 7/5/1932.
18. Manning, McDowell, op. cit., p. 88.
19. M. Kennedy, *Divisions & Consensus, The Politics of Cross Boarder Relations in Ireland* (Dublin 2000), pp. 39–41.
20. Manning, McDowell, op. cit., p. 124.
21. Government White Paper Report on Rural Electrification (1944).
22. ESB Archive, Dublin; *Role of Electricity Supply Board* (1973).
23. ESB Archive, Dublin; video, 'P.J. Dowling Carlow Man of the Year 1998.'
24. M. Shiel, *The Quite Revolution; The Electrification of Rural Ireland 1946–1976* (Dublin 1984).
    M. Daly, 'Turn on the Tap: The State, Irish Women and Running Water' in M. O'Dowd, M. Valiulis (eds), *Engendering Irish History: Essays in Honour of Margaret MacCurtain* (Dublin 1997).
25. Manning, McDowell, op. cit., p. 123.
26. McLaughlin 'Presidential Address 1950' *Trans. Inst. Civil Engineers,* November 1950.
27. ESB Archive, Dublin; *Electrical Journal*, March 1971.
28. ESB Archive, Dublin; Letter from P.P. O'Reilly, RTE, to Miss Prinny McLaughlin, 24/2/1971.

■ Schoen, 'The Irish Free State and the Electricity Industry, 1922–1927'

1. L. Schoen, *Studien zur Entwicklung hydro-elektrischer Energienutzung: Die Elektrifizierung Irlands* (Düsseldorf 1979), pp. 68–170, 217–32. This is an abridged version of part of the book. Those seeking greater detail on sources, bibliography and the Siemens business records should consult it. For a general background to the Irish electricity industry prior to the Shannon Scheme and the history of the ESB see M. Manning & M. McDowell, *Electricity Supply in Ireland. The History of the ESB* (Dublin 1984).
2. RTE film, '40 Light Years from Parteen' (1967). *The Electrification of the Irish Free State. The Shannon Scheme. Report of the Experts appointed by the Government* (Dublin 1925), p. 8.
3. T. McLaughlin, *The Shannon Scheme Considered in its National Economic Aspect* (Dublin 1925), p. 39. M. Matolcsi 'Irország villamosítása és a Shannon-i vizerőtelep', *Technika* 10 (1929), p. 3.
4. Matolcsi, loc. cit., p. 3. RTE film, op. cit. *Report of the Experts*, op cit., p. 3.
5. McLaughlin, op. cit., p. 12.
6. ESB Archives, Dublin; *Report of the Experts*, op. cit., p. 7.
7. McLaughlin, op. cit., p. 12.
8. J. Murphy, 'Hydro-Electric Undertaking at Bandon', *Trans. Inst. Civil Engineers of Ireland*, vol. LI, 1924–5 (1926), p. 22. J. Murphy 'The Bandon Hydro-Electric Undertaking', *The Electrical Review*, 9 January 1925, p. 77.
9. Schoen, op. cit., pp. 99–100.
10. *Seanad Debates,* vol. 1 (1923), 1067.
11. ESB Archives, Dublin; *Report of the Experts*, op. cit., p. 112.
12. These included the 'Dublin and District Electricity Supply Bill' of the Corporation of Dublin, 'Dublin Electricity Supply Bill' of the Anna Liffey Power Development Co. Ltd., and 'East Leinster Electricity Supply Bill' of J.F. Crowley and Partners, Liffey-Shannon Project. *Dáil Debates,* vol. 7 (1924), 1157, 1163–7, 1173.
13. ESB Archives, Dublin; Saorstát Éireann, Dublin Electricity Supply Bill, 1924 and 1925.
14. *The Irish Builder and Engineer*, 76 (1934), no. 23, 17 November, supplement.
15. McLaughlin had particularly close contact to Minister E. McNeill, who recommended his plans to other members of the government. *Irish Times*, 10/4/1976. RTE interview (1967).
16. *Dáil Debates,* vol. 10 (1925), 2015. RTE interview (1967), where McLaughlin commented: 'He had a great deal of other things on his mind … he was not very interested.'
17. Siemens Archives, Munich (SA hereafter): 35–22/Ls 454. 'The Electrification of the Irish Free State. The Shannon Scheme developed by Siemens-Schuckert' (1924).

18. *Dáil Debates,* vol. 9 (1924), 2791–2859, 3530, vol. 10 (1925), 2047. *The Irish Builder and Engineer,* 66 (1924), p. 845.

19. SA; 21/Lb 605, 35/Lk 287. Also see *Report of the Experts,* op. cit. R. Fanning, *The Irish Department of Finance 1922-58* (Dublin 1978), pp. 179-86,188-92.

20. In the Dáil, the Shannon Electricity bill, as with all subsequent bills relating to electrical supply in the country, had to pass the usual five stages for a public bill: First Stage, Second Stage, Third (Committee) Stage, Fourth (Report) Stage and Fifth (Final) Stage. The most important stages were the two readings in the Second Stage and in Committee Stage with extensive discussions and debates. The Seanad with its limited power could not prevent the implementation of legislation, but could delay it.

21. *Daily Mail,* 3/7/1924.

22. 'The Shannon Hydro-Electric Power Scheme', *The Engineer,* Reprint Part 1, 2 December 1927– 30 March 1928, p. 3: 'In spite of opinions that have been expressed on the placing of the contract with a German firm, an impartial consideration … shows clearly that the reason is to be found in the initiative and enterprise of Siemens-Schuckert in putting forward their proposals, and in the care and energy displayed in convincing the experts and the Government that the technical and economic bases of the proposals were sound. If any English firm had tackled the matter in the same way, there seems to be no doubt that it would have been given equal opportunities, and the money that is being spent on the undertaking might have come to this country.' *The Electrical Review,* 24/4/1925, p. 25.

    A few years later *The Observer* noted that the Irish–German partnership had been a success: 'No charge of feebleness … can be laid at the door of the Irish Free State Government in tentatively accepting the proposals laid before them by the German firm of Siemens-Schuckert, nor can any charge of want of care or of political bias be advanced in respect of the manner in which these proposals were examined and tested.' 29/9/1929.

23. *Dáil Debates,* vol. 10 (1925), 1789, 1798–9, 1810, 1824.

24. *Dáil Debates,* vol. 9 (1924), 2791–2859, 3499.

25. These two reports, or extracts from them, were only available to the public from February/March 1925. J. M. Fay, 'Economic Aspects of the Shannon Power Development', TICEI vol. LIV, 1927–28 (1929), p. 38.

26. ESB Archives, Dublin; *Report of the Experts,* op. cit., p. 118.

27. *Dáil Debates,* vol. 9 (1924), 3552.

28. *The Irish Builder and Engineer,* 66 (1924), pp. 406–8.

29. *Dáil Debates,* vol. 6 (1924), 2730. This continues: 'If Messrs. Siemens can satisfy experts of their ability to distribute from the Shannon power in sufficient quantity at an economic price and a minimum capital cost for the whole Free State, there is no need to invite other firms to put forward a similar scheme.'

30. National Archives; Department of Foreign Affairs file 385.

31. *Seanad Debates,* vol. 4 (1925), 1048.

32. *Dáil Debates,* vol. 11 (1925), 1713.

33. McGilligan pointed out: 'Not a single penny will go from the Irish government to the Siemens-Schuckert firm under paragraph 13, and I can produce letters from the firm agreeing with that.' *Seanad Debates,* vol. 4 (1925), 1043.

34. Two comments by Cosgrave and McGilligan provide further illumination on the intentions of the Cabinet on this procedure. Cosgrave on 2 April 1924 pointed out (*Dáil Debates,* vol. 6 (1924), 2731): 'Rigid adherence to such a procedure would rule out of consideration any such offer as that made by Messrs. Siemens to satisfy experts that a national scheme, based on the Shannon, is practicable, and would consequently restrict unduly the possibilities of electrical development.' McGilligan said on 31 March 1925 (*Seanad Debates,* vol. 4 (1925), 1043) that the White Paper was unusual but necessary: 'Unless it was unusual there would be no Shannon Scheme. One had to get out of the methods that tied people hand and foot formerly before any such schemes could be produced.'

35. Sir John P. Griffith, *Further Notes on the Siemens-Schuckert Shannon Power Scheme* (Dublin 1925), p. 4.

36. *Dáil Debates,* vol. 11 (1925), 127.

37. National Archives; Department of Foreign Affairs file 385. Letter T.A. Smiddy, Washington, of 27 May 1925, to E. N. Hurley, Chicago, in answer to Hurley's letter to Smiddy of 15 May 1925.

38. National Archives; Department of Foreign Affairs file 385. Memo McGilligan of 16 June 1925 to Minister for External Affairs FitzGerald.

39. *Dáil Debates*, vol. 9 (1924), 2856–7. R. Davis, *Arthur Griffith and Non-Violent Sinn Féin* (Dublin 1974), pp. 127–8.

40. Before 1925, all the legislative enactments covering the generation and distribution of electricity in the Free State had originated from the time when Ireland formed part of the United Kingdom; they applied in Ireland largely in the same way as in England, Scotland and Wales. With the Government of Ireland Act, 1920, and the Irish Free State (Agreement) Act, 1922, provisions were made by Britain for the transfer of the administration of the public supply utilities to the governments of 'Southern Ireland' (i.e. the Irish Free State) and Northern Ireland. J. Shiress Will and J.C. Dalton (eds), *The Law Relating to Electric Lighting, Power and Traction* (London 1927), p. 55.

41. ESB Archives, Dublin; Annual Report of the ESB 12 (1938/39), p. 6.

42. *Dáil Debates,* vol. 10 (1925), 1753, 1822, 1829.

43. *Dáil Debates,* vol. 11 (1925), 1783. Also see M. Maguire, 'The Space of the Nation: History, Culture and a Conflict in Modern Ireland', *Irish Studies Review,* vol. 6, no. 2 (1998), pp. 109–20.

44. *Dáil Debates,* vol. 10 (1925), 1837.

45. *Dáil Debates,* vol. 11 (1925), 926, 1767, 2217.

46. For example, Major J. Myles made the assertion that products of the German electrical industry were known to be inferior to those of many other countries, and because of inadequate safety standards less reliable than English or American; the project should therefore preferably not be entrusted to a German firm. In addition, there would be too much dependence on a few firms for necessary spare parts supply. *Dáil Debates,* vol. 10 (1925), 1980.

47. Sir John P. Griffith, *Notes on the Siemens-Schuckert Shannon Power Scheme* (Dublin 1925).

48. *Encyclopaedia of Ireland* (Dublin 1968), p. 412.

49. Sir John P. Griffith, *Engineering Reminiscences* (1936), pp. 265–89.

50. *Dáil Debates,* vol. 11 (1925), 1852; T. Johnson, 2215: 'I believe that the scheme … will generate a new spirit through generating a new environment! I believe the social value of this scheme is of even more importance than the economic value, but I believe the economic value to be great.'

51. *Dáil Debates,* vol. 11 (1925), 882, 1188.

52. *The Irish Statesman,* 11/4/1925, p. 133.

53. E. Rumpf, *Nationalismus und Sozialismus in Irland* (Meisenheim am Glan 1959), p. 96. See E. Rumpf and A.C. Hepburn, *Nationalism and Socialism in Twentieth Century Ireland* (Liverpool 1977).

54. *Seanad Debates,* vol. 4 (1925), 1013, 1015, 1018.

55. *Seanad Debates,* vol. 5 (1925), 368.

56. *Irish Times,* 19/2/1973.

57. He made a comparison with Switzerland: 'In Switzerland … there is no such big unified power scheme as this.' *Seanad Debates,* vol. 4 (1925), 1026.

58. *Seanad Debates,* vol. 5 (1925), 264, 288, 718. P. Sweeney, *The Politics of Public Enterprise and Privatisation* (Dublin 1990), p. 17.

59. The Earl of Longford and T. P. O'Neill, *Eamon de Valera* (London 1974), p. 268.

60. *Dáil Debates,* vol. 18 (1927), 1897.

61. National Archives; S.P.O. DT/S 4735, Memoranda McGilligan, dated 14 December 1925 and dated 15 December 1926. *Dáil Debates,* vol. 18 (1927), 1903.

62. National Archives; S.P.O. DT/S 4735, Memo McGilligan dated 15 December 1926. H. Hoover, 'Government Policies in Relation to Power Development and Distribution', *The Transactions of the First WPC* (London 1924), vol. iv, pp. 1580-90 (p. 1589: 'It is the business of Government to regulate and control, not to manage or operate.': p. 1590: 'The Government can best contribute through stimulation of and cooperation with voluntary forces in our national life …').

63. *Dáil Debates,* vol. 18 (1927), 1899, 1908. National Archives; S.P.O. DT/S 4735, extract from a letter

of McGilligan from Sweden, 8 September 1926, to K. O'Higgins. Memo. H.P. Boland, Department of Finance, 3 January 1927. Memo J. J. McElligott, Department of Finance, 7 January 1927.

64. *Dáil Debates,* vol. 18 (1927), 1898, 1904, 1906, 1908.
65. National Archives; S.P.O. DT/S 4735, Memo. H.P. Boland, 3 January 1927.
66. ESB Archives, Dublin: Annual Report of the ESB 1 (1927/28), p. 5.
67. Saorstát Éireann, Electricity (Supply) Act, 1927, p. 52.
68. The model of the ESB as a semi-state body was used frequently by the state in the following decades; by 1975 there were almost fifty.
69. *The Role of the Electricity Supply Board* (Dublin 1973), p. 5.
70. According to official information, there were at the start of 1927 in the Free State 110 suppliers of electricity who could be designated as public electricity supply undertakings: 20 'statutory undertakings' (of monopolistic character, within well-defined boundaries, but subject to certain regulations; 15 of these in municipal or communal hands, and 5 privately owned) and 90 'non-statutory undertakings' (almost all in private ownership). If operations which generated their own electricity, and incidentally also supplied others, are included, then the number of the 'non-statutory undertakings' rose to 300 (which were mostly very small plants). National Archives; S.P.O. DT/S 4735. *Dáil Debates,* vol. 18 (1927), 1895. McLaughlin, op. cit., p. 12.
71. In addition, large amounts were due under Section 12.2. of the Act of 1927 for the payment of interest on the advances to the special Shannon Fund from the Minister for Finance (up to £600, 000), which together with expenditure for operation, maintenance and repairs on the Shannon installation, was included in the £5.21 million of the Shannon Electricity Act, 1925; this stipulation of the Section 12.2. was later superseded in the Electricity (Finance) Act, 1929, which specified for the ESB the sum of £156, 000 for these purposes.
72. ESB Archives, Dublin; Annual Report of the ESB 1 (1927/28), p. 12. The ESB attached huge significance to these marketing measures. Annual report of the ESB 2 (1928/29), p. 18: '… the Board realised that the education of the public as to the progress and possibilities of the Shannon Scheme was essential to the success of the scheme.'
73. E.A. Lawler, 'Public Relations', *Administration,* vol. 5, No. 3 (1957), p. 149.
74. The advertisements promoted both the visits to Ardnacrusha, and the advantages of the use of electricity. One example from 1928, how electrical energy relieves workers and farmers of heavy and time-consuming manual labour: 'The American workman is the most prosperous on earth, because he has, on an average, three horse-power, the equivalent of thirty human slaves, helping him to produce.' *The Role of the ESB,* p. 4.
75. ESB Archives, Dublin; Annual Reports of the ESB 2 (1928/29), 5 (1931/32).
76. ESB Archives, Dublin; Annual Reports of the ESB 1 (1927/28), p. 12, 2 (1928/29), p. 19; also see Lawler (1957), p. 151. The film was shot in summer 1928 by the First National Pathé Film Company, and shown in the subsequent months in cinemas, schools, universities etc. in Ireland, Great Britain and the USA.
77. ESB Archives, Dublin; Annual Report of the ESB 2 (1928/29), p. 20. Lawler (1957), p. 151.
78. G. O'Beirne, *Siemens in Ireland 1925–2000. Seventy-five Years of Innovation* (Dublin 2000).
79. On 31 March 1929 the ESB already had 829 employees. ESB Archives, Dublin; Annual Report of the ESB 2 (1928/29), p. 21.
80. *Irish Times,* 6/4/1976.

■ **McCarthy, 'How the Shannon Scheme Workers Lived'**

1. *Irish Times,* 14/8/1925.
2. *Irish Independent,* 1/9/1925. Irish Railway Record Society, Dublin; Record Book of the Great Southern and Western Railway, 1924–27. A number of the Siemens employees arrived at Queenstown (Cobh)

from Germany in 1925 and 1926, travelling on by rail to Limerick. Some were detained or sent back because they did not have work permits.

3. *Limerick Leader*, 26/9/1925. *Irish Times*, 29/9/1925.
4. *Irish Times*, 29/9/1925.
5. *Voice of Labour*, 29/10/1925.
6. *Voice of Labour*, 5/12/1925.
7. *Voice of Labour*, 7/11/1925.
8. *Clare Champion*, 8/5/1926.
9. *Limerick Leader*, 5/10/1928.
10. *Limerick Leader*, 7/1/1927.
11. *Engineer*, 16/12/1927.
12. *Clare Champion*, 3/7/1926.
13. *Fifty Years of Shannon Power*, ESB Golden Jubilee publication.
14. *Voice of Labour*, 9/5/1926.
15. *Limerick Leader*, 9/5/1928.
16. *Limerick Leader*, 30/6/1926.
17. *Clare Champion*, 8/5/1926. *Limerick Leader*, 10/4/1926.
18. *Clare Champion*, 8/5/1926.
19. *Clare Champion*, 3/7/1926.
20. Ibid.
21. *Irish Independent*, 26/6/1926.
22. *Irish Independent*, 29/6/1926.
23. *Limerick Leader*, 21/4/1926.
24. *Voice of Labour*, 2/1/1926.
25. *Voice of Labour*, 3/7/1926.
26. *Voice of Labour*, 12/6/1926.
27. M. McCarthy, 'The Shannon Scheme Strike', *Old Limerick Journal*, December 1980, pp. 21–6.
28. *Voice of Labour*, 24/4/1926, 26/6/1926.
29. *Dáil Debates*, 16, 1902–1904.
30. *Dáil Debates*, 16/2017–2018.
31. *Dáil Debates*, 16/2020.
32. *Dáil Debates*, 16/2022.
33. *Dáil Debates*, 16/2024.
34. *Dáil Debates*, 16/2023.
35. *Dáil Debates*, 16/2032/2034.
36. Ibid.
37. *Irish Times*, 2/7/1926. *Limerick Leader*, 5/7/1926. *Clare Champion*, 17/7/1926.
38. *Irish Times*, 12/7/1926.
39. *Clare Champion*, 17/7/1926.
40. *Limerick Leader*, 12/7/1926.
41. *Clare Champion*, 17/7/1926.
42. *Clare Champion*, 28/8/1926.
43. *Limerick Leader*, 27/7/1926.
44. *Limerick Leader*, 6/10/1926.
45. *Clare Champion*, 9/10/1926.
46. Ibid.
47. Ibid.
48. *Limerick Leader*, 8/2/1928
49. *Clare Champion*, 4/2/1928.
50. *Clare Champion*, 18/2/1928.
51. *Limerick Leader*, 15/10/1928.
52. *Voice of Labour*, 2/1/1926.
53. National Archives: Department of Finance, 5/7/11/26.

UCD Archives: McGilligan Papers, pp. 35/78

54. *Limerick Leader*, 14/11/1927.
55. *Limerick Leader*, 25/4/1928.
56. *Limerick Leader*, 28/11/1928.
57. *Limerick Leader*, 21/4/1928.
58. *Limerick Leader*, 16/10/1926.
59. *Limerick Leader*, 5/9/1927.
60. *Limerick Leader*, 14/10/1927.
61. *Limerick Leader*, 24/12/1928.
62. *Limerick Leader*, 12/1/1929, 4/5/1929.

■ **O'Beirne & O'Connor, 'Siemens-Schuckert and the Electrification of the Irish Free State'**

1. Extracted and translated from L. Schoen (ed.), *Studien zur Entwicklung hydroelectrischer Enegienutzung: Die Electrifizierung Irlands* (Düsseldorf 1979). For a history of Siemens in Ireland, see G. O'Beirne, *Siemens in Ireland 1925–2000* (Dublin 2000). For a history of Siemens AG see W. Feldenkirchen, *Siemens: From Workshop to Global Player* (Munich 2000).
2. Siemens Archive, Munich (hereafter SA), 35–22/Ls 454.
3. National Archives; Department of Foreign Affairs file 385.
4. SA, 21/Lb 605.
5. P. Hellersberg, 'Deutschlands grösster Auslandsauftrag' in *Auslandswarte* (1927), p. 117. P. Hellersberg, 'Auf der grünen Insel', *Ikarus*, April 1929, p. 20.
6. SA, 68/Li 233.
7. SA, 35–22/Ls 454.
8. O. Uitting, *Generalplanung von Wasserkraftanlagen* (Berlin 1953), p. 187.
9. ESB Archives, Dublin; *The Electrification of the Irish Free State* (1924), pp. 145, 167.
10. Ibid., p. 171. R. Fischer, H. Beil, 'Die Elektrizitätsversorgung der Landwirtschaft', *Das Zeitalter der Elektrizität* (1967), p. 153.
11. ESB Archives, Dublin; *The Shannon Scheme developed by SSW*, p. 178.
12. Ibid., p. 1.
13. *Dáil Debates*, vol. 9 (1924), 2829–2831; SA, 21/Lb 605.
14. SA, 35/Lk 287.
15. Ibid., p. 66.
16. Ibid., pp. 88, 119.
17. ESB Archives, Dublin; *The Shannon Scheme developed by SSW*, unabriged, esp. pp. 109, 138, 215, 268, 272, 297, 309, 312, 315; for the electrical part, see also SA, 35–22/Ls 454.
18. The unit of currency in Germany until the end of the Second World War, roughly equivalent to a shilling (one twentieth of a pound sterling).
19. L. Reichard, M. Enzweiler, 'Die Elektrifizierung Irlands und der Ausbau des Shannon', *Siemens Jahrbuch* (1927), p. 48.
20. Ibid., p. 34.
21. SA, 21/Lb 605.
22. SA, 4/Lf 678.
23. SA, 11/Lf 180.
24. SA, 21/Lb 605. *Dáil Debates,* vol. 10 (1925), 2031.
25. SA, 21/Lb 605.
26. National Archives; Department of Foreign Affairs, file 385.
27. National Archives; S.P.O. DT/S 4380/2.
28. Ibid., SA, 15/Le 6, SA 20/Le 139.
29. National Archive; S.P.O. DT/S 4380/2.
30. *Irish Independent*, 23/6/1929. *The Times*, 22/7/1929.

31. *Irish Independent,* 23/7/1929.
32. Ibid.
33. A. Bürklin, *Entwicklung der Freileitungen bis zu den Hochspannungsstrassen der neuzeitlichen Energiewirtschaft* (1943), p. 11. SA, 47/Lg 782.
34. Schoen, op. cit., pp. 68–317.
35. SA, 21/Lb 605.
36. Siemens Ltd, Dublin; 'Final Account', 16 August 1930, and 'Engineer's Final Certificate', 21 October 1930, file.
37. SA, 11/Lg 700.
38. Schoen (1979), pp. 68–317.
39. SA, 17/Le 86.
40. SA, 11/Lo 738.
41. SA, 4/Lf 678; SA, 21/Lb 605.
42. SA, 11/Lf 180.
43. Schoen, op.cit., pp. 68–317.
44. Ibid.
45. SA, 4/Lf 678.
46. Ibid., SA, 11/Lg 700.
47. SA, 4/Lf 678.
48. Schoen, op. cit., pp. 68–317.
49. SA, 4/Lf 678.
50. National Archives; S.P.O. DT/S 4380/2. As in the meantime (in September 1931) the pound had been devalued by some 30 per cent relative to the RM, this amount was now no longer equivalent to more than 3 million RM, but to only somewhat more than 2 million RM.
51. SA, 4/Lf 678.
52. SA, 15/Le 465 & 17/Le 102. S&H was a participant with SSW in SBU, and was also a parent company of SSW.
53. Schoen, op. cit., pp. 68–317.
54. SA, 17/Le 102.
55. Schoen, op. cit., pp. 68–317.
56. Ibid.
57. SA, 4/Lf 678.
58. *Dáil Debates,* vol. 31(1929), 366.
59. ESB Archives; ESB Annual Report (1930/31), p. 7.
60. *Dáil Debates,* vol. 43 (1932), 235.
61. Schoen, op. cit., pp. 68–317.
62. *Dáil Debates,* vol. 39 (1931), 1694.
63. Ibid., 1709.
64. *Seanad Debates,* vol. 14 (1931), 1688.
65. *Seanad Debates,* vol. 24 (1940), 2731.
66. O'Beirne (2000), p. 67.

■ **Delany, 'The Railway System for the Shannon Scheme'**

1. G. O'Beirne, *History of Siemens in Ireland 1925–2000* (Dublin 2000), p. 50. The technical details of the railway network for the Shannon Scheme are perhaps best captured by Dr Georg Garbotz in 'The Plant & Machinery in Use on the Construction of the Shannon Power Works', *Trans. Inst. Civil Engineers,* vol. 53 (1927).
2. Irish Railway Society Archive, Dublin; Great Southern & Western Railway, Record of Translantic Traffic 1924–1927. This reveals a number of engineers arrived at Cobh from Germany on US-bound ships, and some were detained or turned back because they did not have a work permit.
3. *The Structural Engineer,* December 1927.

4. W. Feldkirchen, *Siemens from Workshop to Global Player* (Munich 2000), p. 207.
5. ESB Archive, Dublin; Siemens-Schuckert, 'The Electrification of the Irish Free State' (1924).
6. ESB Archive, Dublin; Siemens-Schuckert, 'Progess on the Shannon', Report no. 12, September (1929).
7. W. Mc Grath, 'Narrow Gauge Railways of the Shannon Scheme', *Narrow Gauge*, no. 75, Spring 1977.
8. Garbotz, op. cit.
9. Paul Duffy, 'Ardnacrusha Birthplace of ESB', *The North Munster Antiquarian Journal*, vol. 29 (1987).
10. Garbotz, op. cit.
11. M. McCarthy, 'The Shannon Scheme Railway', *Reflections on Munster Railways* (Limerick 1984).
12. M. Manning & M. McDowell, *History of ESB* (Dublin 1984), p. 45.
13. H. Dougherty, 'Shannon Discovery', *Railway Magazine* (August 1988).
14. *Limerick Leader*, 7/5/1927.
15. ESB Archive, Dublin; Siemens-Schuckert, op.cit.

■ Bielenberg, 'Seán Keating, the Shannon Scheme, and the Art of State-Building'

1. I would like to thank Gemma Bradley for permission to quote from her thesis; Justin Keating and the late Michael Keating for interviews and some source material; Linda Connolly and Tom Dunne for commenting on earlier drafts. The views expressed and any mistakes are mine.
2. S.B. Kennedy, *Great Irish Artists* (Dublin 1997), p. 96.
3. H. Sharpe, *Michael Kane: His Life and Art* (Dublin 1983), p. 22.
4. B. Fallon, *Irish Art 1830–1990* (Belfast 1994), pp. 111–13.
5. P. Murray, 'Irish Painting, Tradition, and Post-War Internationalism' in J. Steward, *When Time Began to Rant and Rage: Figurative Painting from Twentieth-Century Ireland* (London 1998), p. 80.
6. F. Cullen, *Visual Politics: The Representation of Ireland 1750–1930* (Cork 1997), pp. 160–74.
7. L.M.G. Bradley, 'John Keating 1889–1977' (unpublished MA, UCD 1991), remains the most comprehensive treatment of his life.
8. J. Turpin, *A School of Art in Dublin since the Eighteenth Century* (Dublin 1995), p. 250.
9. T. Snoddy, *Dictionary of Irish Artists; 20th Century* (Dublin 1996), p. 229.
10. Bradley, op. cit., pp. 13–14. T. O'Callaghan, 'Profile; Sean Keating', *Image*, November 1977, p. 45.
11. *Limerick Leader*, 26/2/1972. He mentions houses in Cecil St, George's St, 1 Clareview Tce, and 4 Newenham St. He described his father as somebody who could never make a decision, something of a dreamer. O'Callaghan, op. cit. Talk by Justin Keating on 'Keating and Ardnacrusha', May, UCC 2000 Conference. Justin suggests that his father was inclined to understate his social background, even to 'proletarianise' it.
12. *Limerick Leader*, 26/2/1977; *Irish Press*, 22/12/1977.
13. *Irish Independent*, 6/6/1973.
14. *Limerick Leader*, 26/2/1972; M. Keating, 'John Keating would rather have the Key Men', *The Engineers Journal*, September/October 1985, pp. 49–51.
15. *Irish Times*, 19/4/1959; J. Turpin, 'William Orpen as Student and Teacher', *Studies*, lxviii (1979), pp. 173–92; O'Callaghan, op. cit.; Keating, op. cit.
16. *Irish Independent*, 6/6/1973.
17. N. Bowe, *Harry Clarke* (Mountrath 1983), pp. 25, 37, 40, 121; O'Callaghan, op. cit., p. 46.
18. B. Arnold, *Orpen: Mirror to an Age* (London 1981), pp. 168, 170, 284–96. Keating revealed a month before his own death that 'I have loved him [Orpen] all my life. He is in my prayers every night' (p. 171).
19. Turpin (1979), pp. 173–92; Turpin (1995), pp. 221, 336.
20. L. O'Broin, *Just Like Yesterday: An Autobiography* (Dublin 1985), p. 23.
21. She was another student of Orpen, and an active nationalist then raising funds for the 1916 prisoners' dependents. See H. Pyle, *Estella Solomons: Portraits of Patriots* (Naas 1966).
22. TCD MS 4631/420 O'Sullivan Papers, Keating to Solomons, 26 May 1917. On the connections between his interest in the nationalist movement as subject matter, see *Limerick Leader*, 26/2/1972; he 'got interested in the nationalistic movement, particularly for what it could offer in portrait figures'.
23. *Limerick Leader*, 26/2/1972.

24. TCD, Bodkin Papers, 6941/439, Keating to Bodkin, 11 December 1918, 6941/441, 17 December 1918.
25. *Image*, November 1977; *Limerick Leader*, 26/2/1972.
26. Bradley, op. cit., pp. 62–6. The large house in the background of his painting 'Allegory' was Woodtown Manor.
27. J. Skehan, 'Seán Keating; Palette and Palate', *The Word*, April 1965.
28. Bradley, op. cit., p. 62.
29. Agreement between Seán Keating and the Hospitals Trust Ltd., 1 January 1934. Document in possession of the late Michael Keating, Áit an Chuain, Rathfarnham.
30. Keating, Retrospective Exhibition, *Éire Ireland;* Weekly Bulletin of Deptartment of External Affairs, no. 624, 24-vi (1963).
31. TCD, Bodkin Papers Ms 6941/443, Keating to Rev. Father, 14 December 1921.
32. O'Snoddy, op. cit., pp. 227–9; P. Butler, *Three Hundred Years of Irish Watercolours and Drawings* (London 1990), p. 183.
33. See photograph of Men of the South in J. Steward, *When Time Began to Rant and Rage: Figurative Paintings from Twentieth Century Ireland* (London 1998), p. 170. See in particular the Red Dumper in works held by ESB, for which there is corresponding colour film taken by Keating at ESB Scheme at Phoulaphouca.
34. M. Maguire, 'The Space of the Nation; History Culture and a Conflict in Modern Ireland', *Irish Studies Review,* vol. 6, no. 2 (1998), pp. 110–12.
35. See for example T. Ryan, 'Seán Keating and Electricity Supply Board', Keating and ESB, Exhibition at Arnacrusha, 1989; Steward, op. cit., p. 186.
36. TCD; Bodkin Papers, Ms 6941/444, Keating to Bodkin, 18 January 1927.
37. A. Stewart, *Royal Hibernian Academy of Arts; Index of Exhibitors 1826–1979* (Dublin 1987), vol. 2, p. 140.
38. *Irish Times*, 6/5/1929.
39. Personal communication with Oldham Art Gallery, 14/9/2001. At a later date the ESB acquired a copy of this painting.
40. Bradley, op. cit, p. 100.
41. Keating, op. cit., p. 49; interview with Michael Keating; Stewart, op. cit., vol. 2, p. 140; M. Manning and M. McDowell (eds), *Electricity Supply in Ireland; The History of the ESB* (Dublin 1984), pp. 44, 88; Letter to Bodkin, op. cit., 18. January 1927.
42. *Irish Times*, 11/5/1929. Justin Keating remembers that after the war Sean had an epidiascope, which he could roll from frame to frame manually, which he may have used earlier (interview with Justin Keating, 1998).
43. Keating, op. cit., pp. 49–51.
44. This photograph has been reproduced in M. McCarthy, 'How the Shannon Scheme Workers Lived', *Old Limerick Journal*, 8 (1981), p. 11.
45. K. Morrison, 'Looking out, Looking in: Nautical Paintings by Mac Gonigal, Yeats and Keating' in A. Dalsimer, V. Kreilkramp (eds), *America's Eye: Irish Paintings from the Collection Brian P. Burns* (Boston 1996), p. 34. I would like to thank Diarmuid Ó'Giolláin for drawing my attention to this article.
46. McCarthy, op. cit., pp. 5–11.
47. Turpin, op. cit., pp. 335–6; Arnold (1981), p. 170.
48. Cullen, op. cit., p. 169; *Irish Times*, 6/5/1929.
49. S.B. Kennedy, op. cit., pp. 96–103. *Irish Times*, 6/5/1929. Cullen, op. cit., p. 169.
50. *Irish Times*, 6/5/1929. The journalist in this instance wrote that Keating was then living in 'his gaily painted cottage in the Dublin Mountains some distance above the Hell Fire Club … when I called late in the evening a young Dubliner who had posed for the gunman in the picture had just arrived with one of the London papers'. He also points out that there is not a German in the picture, and that central figure was 'any businessman, who, not unnaturally, is quite contemptuous of the gunman'.
51. B. Hobson (ed.), *Irish Free State Official Handbook* (Dublin 1932). The watercolour 'Ardnacrusha' displayed at the 'Sean Keating Exhibition' at the RHA Gallagher Gallery (Dublin 1989) is in private hands, and it is probably one of a number not in the ESB Collection.

52. Keating, op. cit., p. 49.
53. Turpin, op. cit., pp. 282, 297, 333, 405. See National Archives, S. 3458.
54. *The New York Times Magazine,* 12/1/1930.
55. D. Ó Giolláin, *Locating Irish Folklore: Tradition, Modernity, Identity* (Cork 2000), pp. 64, 78.

■ Cullen, 'Some Notable Features of the Design and Operational History of Ardnacrusha since 1929'

1. The ESB moved its national control centre from Ardnacrusha to Dublin in 1954.
2. C. O'Riordan, 'Development of Ireland's Power System 1927 to 1997' (Dublin 2000).
3. ESB Archives, Dublin; ESB Annual Reports.
4. Staff file.
5. ESB Archives, Dublin; ESB Annual Reports.
6. L. Schoen, *Studein: Die Electifizierung Irlands* (Düsseldorf 1979).
7. Report on Tests with New Runner, Unit No. 1, Ardnacrusha, 7 October 1937.
8. M. Maguire, 'The Space of the Nation: History Culture and a Conflict in Modern Ireland', *Irish Studies Review,* vol. 6, no. 2 (1998), pp. 113-59.
9. ESB Archives, Dublin; Annual Reports.

Contributors

Andy Bielenberg

Born in Dublin. Studied History at NUI Cork and at post-graduate level in TCD and the LSE. Currently Statutory Lecturer in Economic History in Department of History, NUI Cork. Pamphlet editor for the Irish Economic and Social History Society of Ireland. Author of works on Irish economic and social history, including *The Irish Diaspora* (London 2000), *Locke's Distillery: A History* (Dublin 1993) and *Cork's Industrial Revolution 1780-1880* (Cork 1991).

Brendan Delany

Born in Dublin. Studied History & Economics in UCD, before completing post-graduate studies in DCU and UCD. BA, H.Dip. in Ed., ACIS, MA, MBA. Worked in a variety of roles in ESB, and as a Consultant for the Electricity Corporation of Ghana and as Head of Control in the National Treasury Management Agency. Currently Archive & Heritage Manager in ESB.

Robert Cullen,

C.Eng., F.I.E.I. B.E. (Electrical) UCD 1965. ESB engineering staff on construction of Great Island, Poolbeg 1 & 2 and Tarbert 2. ESB Resident Engineer on Aghada and Moneypoint construction sites. Maintenance Manager, Moneypoint Station. Station Manager, Ardnacrusha and Lee Hydro-electric Stations.

Michael McCarthy

Attended university in NUI Galway, Leeds and Rome. Author of articles on the Shannon Scheme in the *Old Limerick Journal*. An RTE television producer for many years, whose documentary 'The Shannon Scheme' appeared in 1982. Currently writing on the Irish Institute for International Affairs.

Gerald O'Beirne

Born in the west of Ireland, lives in Dublin. Holds degrees from UCD in Engineering and Economics. A member of staff of Siemens for many years, retiring in 1995 as Senior Manager (Power & Automation Division). Author of *Siemens in Ireland 1925-2000* (Dublin 2000).

Michael O'Connor

Lives in Dublin, with a strong interest in industrial history and Honours degrees in Commerce and Marketing from UCD. Employed as Marketing Manager for Siemens Limited (Ireland) and has held senior marketing positions in public and private sector organisations.

Lothar Schoen

Born in 1941. Studied Electrical Engineering and History of Science and Technology at the Technische Universität Berlin (Ph.D. 1979). Joined Siemens Archives in 1978. A member of VDE History Committee since 1980, 'Geschichte der Elektrotechnik' (VDE: Verband Deutscher Elektrotechniker, Association of German Electrical Engineers). Author of works on German electrical engineering, including *Studien zur Entwicklung hydro-elektischer Energienutzung: Die Elektrifizierung Irlands* (Düsseldorf 1979).